Chapters 21–24 Resources

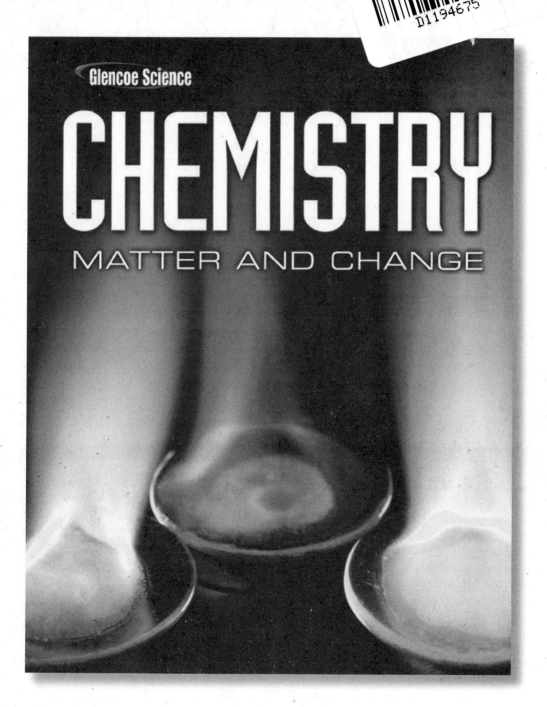

Glencoe Science

CHEMISTRY

MATTER AND CHANGE

Mc Graw Hill **Glencoe**

New York, New York   Columbus, Ohio   Chicago, Illinois   Woodland Hills, California

The *McGraw·Hill* Companies

 Glencoe

Send all inquiries to:
Glencoe/McGraw-Hill
8787 Orion Place
Columbus, OH 43240-4027

ISBN: 978-0-07-878765-2
MHID: 0-07-878765-3

Printed in the United States of America.

2 3 4 5 6 7 8 9 10 045 11 10 09 08

Table of Contents

Chapters 21-24 Resources

Reproducible Student Pages

Teacher Guide and Answers

To the Teacher

This booklet contains resource materials to help you teach more effectively. You will find the following in the chapters:

Reproducible Pages

Hands-on Activities

MiniLab and ChemLab Worksheets: Each activity in this book is an expanded version of each lab that appears in the Student Edition of *Glencoe Chemistry: Matter and Change*. All materials lists, procedures, and questions are repeated so that students can read and complete a lab in most cases without having a textbook on the lab table. All lab questions are reprinted with lines on which students can write their answers. In addition, for student safety, all appropriate safety symbols and caution statements have been reproduced on these expanded pages. Answer pages for each MiniLab and ChemLab are included in the *Teacher Guide and Answers* section at the back of this book.

Transparency Activities

Teaching Transparency Masters and Worksheets: These transparencies relate to major concepts that will benefit from an extra visual learning aid. Most of the transparencies contain art or photos that extend the concepts put forth in the textbook. Others contain art or photos directly from the Student Edition. There are 73 Teaching Transparencies, provided here as black-and-white masters accompanied by worksheets that review the concepts presented in the transparencies. Answers to worksheet questions are provided in the *Teacher Guide and Answers* section at the back of this book.

Math Skills Transparency Masters and Worksheets: These transparencies relate to mathematical concepts that will benefit from an extra visual learning aid. Most of the transparencies contain art or photos directly from the Student Edition, or extend concepts put forth in the textbook. There are 42 Math Skills Transparencies, provided here as black-and-white masters accompanied by worksheets that review the concepts presented in the transparencies. Answers to worksheet questions are provided in the *Teacher Guide and Answers* section at the back of this book.

Intervention and Assessment

Study Guide: These pages help students understand, organize, and compare the main chemistry concepts in the textbook. The questions and activities also help build strong study and reading skills. There are six study guide pages for each chapter. Students will find these pages easy to follow because the section titles match those in the textbook. Italicized sentences in the study guide direct students to the related topics in the text.

The *Study Guide* exercises employ a variety of formats including multiple-choice, matching, true/false, labeling, completion, and short answer questions. The clear, easy-to-follow exercises and the self-pacing format are geared to build your students' confidence in understanding chemistry. Answers or possible responses to all questions are provided in the *Teacher Guide and Answers* section at the back of this book.

Chapter Assessment: Each chapter assessment includes several sections that assess students' understandings at different levels.

- The *Reviewing Vocabulary* section tests students' knowledge of the chapter's vocabulary. A variety of formats are used, including matching, true/false, completion, and comparison of terms.

- The *Understanding Main Ideas* section consists of two parts: Part A tests recall and basic understanding of facts presented in the chapter, while Part B is designed to be more challenging and requires deeper comprehension of concepts than does Part A. Students may be asked to explain chemical processes and relationships or to make comparisons and generalizations.

- The *Thinking Critically* section requires students to use several different higher-order learning skills, such as interpreting data and discovering relationships in graphs and tables, as well as applying their understanding of concepts to solve problems, compare and contrast situations, and to make inferences or predictions.

- The *Applying Scientific Methods* section puts students into the role of researcher. They may be asked to read about an experiment, simulation, or model and then apply their understanding of chapter concepts and scientific methods to analyze and explain the procedure and results. Many of the questions in this section are open-ended, giving students the opportunity to demonstrate both reasoning and creative problem-solving skills.

Answers or possible responses to all questions are provided in the *Teacher Guide and Answers* section at the back of this book.

STP Recording Sheet: Recording Sheets allow students to use the Standardized Test Practice questions in the Student Edition as a practice for standardized tests. STP Recording Sheets give them the opportunity to use bubble answer grids and numbers grids for recording answers. Answers for the STP Recording Sheets can be found in the Teacher Wraparound Edition on *Standardized Test Practice* pages.

Teacher Guide and Answers: Answers or possible answers for questions in this booklet can be found in the *Teacher Guide and Answers* section. Materials, teaching strategies, and content background, along with chapter references, are also provided where appropriate.

Lab Safety Form

Name: _____

Date: _____

Lab type (circle one) : Launch Lab MiniLab ChemLab

Lab Title: _____

Read carefully the entire lab and then answer the following questions. Your teacher must initial this form before you begin the lab.

1. What is the purpose of the investigation?

_____

_____

_____

2. Will you be working with a partner or on a team? _____

3. Is this a design-your-own procedure? Circle: Yes   No

4. Describe the safety procedures and additional warnings that you must follow as you perform this investigation.

_____

_____

_____

5. Are there any steps in the procedure or lab safety symbols that you do not understand? Explain.

_____

_____

_____

Table of Contents

Reproducible Pages

Chapter 21 Hydrocarbons

miniLAB 21

Synthesize and Observe Ethyne

Observe and Infer Why is ethyne used in welding torches?

Materials 150-mL beaker, stirring rod, liquid dishwashing detergent, calcium carbide, forceps, wood splints, matches, ruler about 40 cm long, rubber band, phenolphthalein solution

Procedure 🥽 🧤 🚫 👐 ♨️ 💧

1. Read and complete the lab safety form.
2. Use a rubber band to attach a wood splint to one end of a ruler that is about 40 cm long, so that about 10 cm of the splint extends beyond the ruler.
3. Place 120 mL water in a 150-mL beaker and add 5 mL dishwashing detergent. Mix thoroughly.
4. Use forceps to pick up a pea-sized lump of calcium carbide (CaC_2). Do not touch the CaC_2 with your fingers. **WARNING:** *CaC$_2$ is corrosive; if CaC$_2$ dust touches your skin, wash it away immediately with a lot of water.* Place the lump of CaC_2 in the beaker of detergent solution.
5. Use a match to light the splint while holding the ruler at the opposite end. Immediately bring the burning splint to the bubbles that have formed from the reaction in the beaker. Extinguish the splint after observing the reaction.
6. Use a stirring rod to dislodge a few large bubbles of ethyne. Do they float or sink in air?
7. Rinse the beaker thoroughly, then add 25 mL distilled water and a drop of phenolphthalein solution. Use forceps to place a small piece of CaC_2 in the solution. Observe the results.

_____

Analysis

1. **Infer** What can you infer about the density of ethyne compared to the density of air?

_____

2. **Predict** The reaction of calcium carbide with water yields two products. One is ethyne gas (C_2H_2). What is the other product? Write a balanced chemical equation for the reaction.

_____

_____

_____

CHEMLAB 21

Forensics: Analyze Hydrocarbon Burner Gases

A valve needs to be replaced in the science lab. The custodian says the gas used in the lab is propane, and the chemistry teacher says it is natural gas (methane). Use scientific methods to settle this dispute.

Problem

What type of alkane gas is used in the science laboratory?

Objectives

- **Measure** a volume of gas by water displacement.
- **Measure** the temperature, pressure, and mass at which the volume of the gas was measured.
- **Calculate** the molar mass of the burner gas using the ideal gas equation.

Materials

barometer
thermometer
1-L or 2-L plastic
   soda bottle with
   cap
burner tubing

pneumatic trough
100-mL graduated
   cylinder
balance (0.01g)
paper towels

Safety Precautions

- **Always wear safety goggles and a lab apron.**
- **Be certain that there are no open flames in the lab.**

Pre-Lab

1. Read the entire **CHEMLAB.**

2. Prepare all written materials that you will take into the laboratory. Include safety precautions and procedure notes. Use the data table on the next page.

3. Use the formulas of methane, ethanc, and propane to calculate the compounds' molar masses.

_____

_____

4. Given R and gas pressure, volume, and temperature, show how you will rearrange the ideal gas equation to solve for moles of gas.

_____

_____

_____

5. Suppose that your burner gas contains a small amount of ethane (C_2H_6). How will the presence of this compound affect your calculated molar mass if the burner gas is predominantly:

a. methane

_____

_____

b. propane

_____

_____

6. Use the data table on the next page.

CHEMLAB (21)

Procedure

1. Read and complete the lab safety form.

2. Connect the burner tubing from the gas supply to the inlet of the pneumatic trough. Fill the trough with tap water. Open the gas valve slightly, and let a small amount of gas into the tank to flush the air out of the tubing.

3. Measure the mass of the dry plastic bottle and cap. Record the mass, barometric pressure, and air temperature.

4. Fill the bottle to overflowing with tap water, and screw on the cap. If some air bubbles remain, tap the bottle gently on the desktop until all air has risen to the top. Add more water, and recap the bottle.

5. Place the thermometer in the trough. Invert the capped bottle into the pneumatic trough, and remove the cap while keeping the mouth of the bottle underwater. Hold the mouth of the bottle directly over the inlet opening of the trough.

6. Slowly open the gas valve, and allow gas to enter the inverted bottle until all of the water has been displaced. Close the gas valve immediately. Record the temperature of the water.

7. While the bottle is still inverted, screw on the cap. Remove the bottle from the water, and dry the outside of the bottle.

8. Measure and record the mass of the bottle containing the burner gas.

9. Place the bottle in a fume hood, turn on the exhaust fan, and remove the cap. Compress the bottle several times to expel most of the gas. Refill the bottle to overflowing with water, and determine the volume of the bottle by pouring the water into a graduated cylinder. Record the volume of the bottle.

10. **Cleanup and Disposal** Clean your workspace as directed.

Mass and Volume Data	
Mass of bottle + air (g)	
Mass of air (g)	
Mass of "empty" bottle (g)	
Mass of bottle + collected burner gas (g)	
Mass of collected burner gas (g)	
Barometric pressure (atm)	
Temperature (°C)	
Temperature (K)	
Volume of gas collected (L)	

Analyze and Conclude

1. **Solve** The density of air at 1 atm and 20°C is 1.205 g/L. Use the volume of the bottle to compute the mass of the air the bottle contains. Use gas laws to compute the density of air at the temperature and pressure of your laboratory.

_____

_____

2. **Calculate** the mass of the empty bottle. Calculate the mass of the collected gas. Use the volume of gas, water temperature, and barometric pressure along with the ideal gas law to calculate the number of moles of gas collected. Use the mass of gas and the number of moles to calculate the molar mass of the gas.

_____

_____

CHEMLAB (21)

3. Conclude How does your experimental molar mass compare with the molar masses of methane, ethane, and propane? Infer which gases are in the burner gas in your lab.

_____

_____

4. Error Analysis Suggest possible sources of error in the experiment.

_____

_____

_____

Inquiry Extension

Design an experiment to test how one variable, such as temperature or atmospheric pressure, affects your results.

_____

_____

_____

_____

_____

_____

TEACHING TRANSPARENCY MASTER

63

Isomers

A

$$H\quad CH_2CH_2CH_3$$
$$C=C$$
$$CH_3CH_2CH_2\quad H$$

$$H\quad H$$
$$C=C$$
$$CH_3CH_2CH_2\quad CH_2CH_2CH_3$$

B

$$H\quad H$$
$$C=C$$
$$CH_3CH_2CH_2CH_2\quad H$$

$$H\quad H$$
$$C=C$$
$$CH_3CH_2CH_2\quad CH_3$$

C

$$CH_3CH_2CH_2CHCH_3$$
$$|$$
$$CH_3$$

$$CH_3$$
$$|$$
$$CH_3CH_2CHCH_2CH_3$$

D

$$CH_2CH_3$$
$$|$$
$$CH_3CH_2CH_2-C-CH_3$$
$$|$$
$$H$$

$$CH_2CH_2CH_3$$
$$|$$
$$CH_3CH_2-C-CH_3$$
$$|$$
$$H$$

E

$$CH_3$$
$$|$$
$$CH_3CH_2CCH_3$$
$$|$$
$$CH_3$$

$$CH_3CH_2CH_2CH_2CH_2CH_3$$

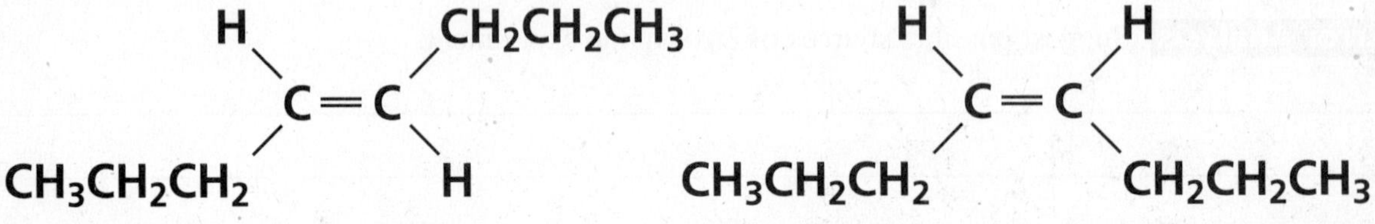

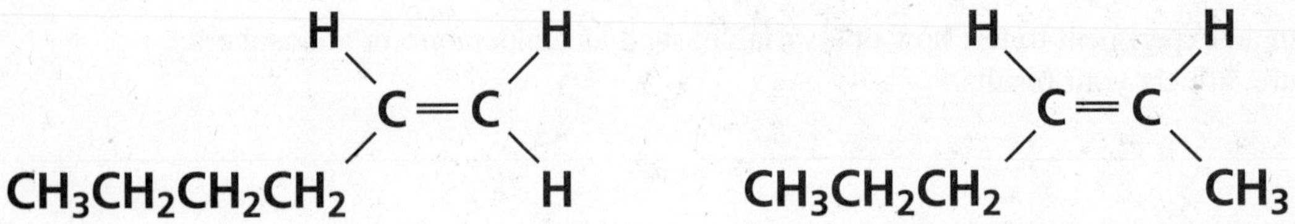

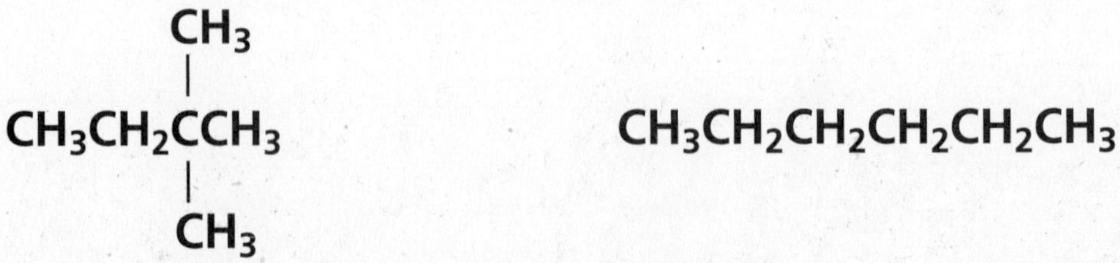

TEACHING TRANSPARENCY WORKSHEET **63**

Isomers

Use with Chapter 21,
Section 21.4

1. Which pair(s) of isomers represent structural isomers?

_____

2. Which pair(s) of isomers represent stereoisomers?

_____

3. Which pair(s) of isomers represent geometric isomers?

_____

4. Which pair(s) of isomers represent optical isomers?

_____

5. Which pair(s) of isomers would you expect to have different melting points, boiling points, and densities?

_____

6. Which pair(s) of isomers would you expect to have different chemical properties? (Include properties related to chemical reactions where chirality is important.)

_____

7. Which pair(s) of isomers would rotate the plane of polarized light in opposite directions?

_____

8. Name the isomers in pair E.

_____

9. Which isomer in pair A is in the *cis-* form, the one on the left or the one on the right?

_____

10. Which pair(s) of isomers have an asymmetric carbon?

_____

TEACHING TRANSPARENCY MASTER

64

Structure of Benzene

**Use with Chapter 21,
Section 21.4**

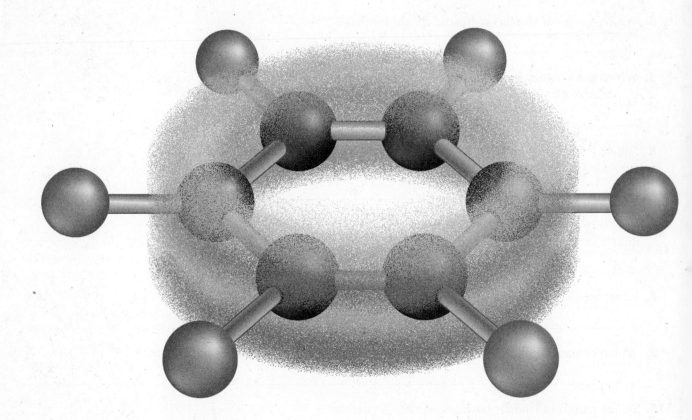

Teaching Transparency Masters

TEACHING TRANSPARENCY WORKSHEET (64)

Structure of Benzene

**Use with Chapter 21,
Section 21.4**

1. How many carbon atoms and hydrogen atoms does a molecule of benzene have?

_____

2. Is benzene a saturated hydrocarbon?

_____

3. What does the double-donut shape on the transparency represent?

_____

_____

4. The drawing below shows what Kekulé proposed for the structure of benzene. How is
   this structure similar to the structure shown on the transparency?

_____

_____

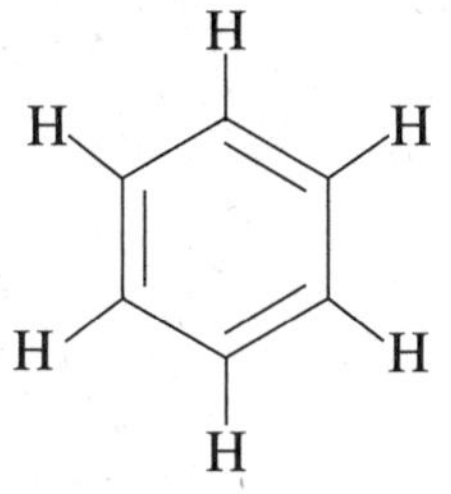

5. How does the structure proposed by Kekulé differ from the structure shown on the
   transparency?

_____

_____

_____

6. If the structure proposed by Kekulé actually existed, would you expect it to be more
   reactive or less reactive than benzene? Why?

_____

_____

_____

7. In the space below, draw another way to represent the structure of benzene that agrees
   with what chemists know about the properties of benzene.

MATH SKILLS TRANSPARENCY MASTER
34

Naming and Drawing Alkanes

**Use with Chapter 21,
Section 21.2**

1. $CH_3CH_2CH_2CH_3$

2. $CH_3CH_2CH_2CH_2CH_2CH_3$

3. $CH_3(CH_2)_8CH_3$

4.
$$CH_3$$
$$|$$
$$CH_3CH_2CHCH_2CH_2CH_3$$

5.
$$CH_3$$
$$|$$
$$CH_3CH_2CH_2CH_2CHCH_3$$

6.
$$CH_2CH_3$$
$$|$$
$$CH_3CH_2CH_2CH_2CHCH_3$$

7.
$$CH_3$$
$$|$$
$$CH_3CH_2CHCH_2CHCH_2CH_3$$
$$|$$
$$CH_3$$

8.
$$CH_2CH_2CH_3$$
$$|$$
$$CH_3CH_2CH_2CCH_2CH_2CH_3$$
$$|$$
$$CH_2CH_3$$

9.
$$CH_2CH_2CH_3$$
$$|$$
$$CH_3CH_2CHCH_2CHCH_2CH_3$$
$$|$$
$$CH_2CH_3$$

10.
$$CH_2CH_3 \quad CH_2CH_3$$
$$| \qquad |$$
$$CH_3CH_2CHCHCH_2CHCHCH_2CH_3$$
$$| \qquad |$$
$$CH_2CH_3 \quad CH_2CH_3$$

11.
$$CH_3 \qquad CH_2CH_2CH_3$$
$$| \qquad\qquad |$$
$$CH_3CH_2CHCHCH_2CHCHCH_2CH_2CH_3$$
$$| \qquad\qquad |$$
$$CH_2CH_3 \quad CH_2CH_3$$

12.

13. CH_3 / CH_3

14. CH_3 / CH_3CH_2

15. 3-methyl-5-propyloctane

16. 3,3,5-trimethylheptane

17. 3-ethyl-4-methyl-6-propylnonane

18. 2-butyl-1,3-diethylcyclopentane

MATH SKILLS TRANSPARENCY WORKSHEET   34

Naming and Drawing Alkanes

**Use with Chapter 21,
Section 21.2**

Name the structures labeled 1 through 14 on the transparency.

1. _____

2. _____

3. _____

4. _____

5. _____

6. _____

7. _____

8. _____

9. _____

10. _____

11. _____

12. _____

13. _____

14. _____

Draw the structures of alkanes 15 through 18 on the transparency.

15.   17.

16.   18.

MATH SKILLS TRANSPARENCY MASTER

Comparing Alkanes, Alkenes, and Alkynes

Use with Chapter 21, Section 21.3

Ethyne
$CH{\equiv}CH$

Ethene
$CH_2{=}CH_2$

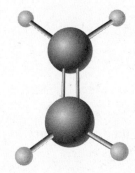

Ethane
CH_3CH_3

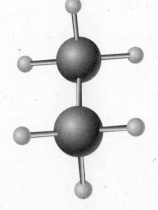

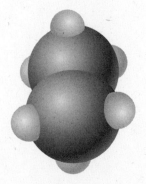

Comparing Alkanes, Alkenes, and Alkynes

Use with Chapter 21, Section 21.3

1. How many carbon and hydrogen atoms are in each of the following alkanes?

    a. ethane, CH_3CH_3 _____ carbons   _____ hydrogens

    b. propane, $CH_3CH_2CH_3$ _____ carbons   _____ hydrogens

    c. butane, $CH_3(CH_2)_2CH_3$ _____ carbons   _____ hydrogens

2. If an alkane has *n* carbon atoms, how many hydrogen atoms will it have?

_____

3. How many carbon and hydrogen atoms are in each of the following alkenes?

    a. ethene, $CH_2{=}CH_2$ _____ carbons   _____ hydrogens

    b. propene, $CH_2{=}CHCH_3$ _____ carbons   _____ hydrogens

    c. 1-butene, $CH_2{=}CHCH_2CH_3$ _____ carbons   _____ hydrogens

4. If an alkene has *n* carbon atoms and one double bond, how many hydrogen atoms will it have?

_____

5. How many carbon and hydrogen atoms are in each of the following alkynes?

    a. ethyne, $CH{\equiv}CH$ _____ carbons   _____ hydrogens

    b. propyne, $CH{\equiv}CCH_3$ _____ carbons   _____ hydrogens

    c. 1-butyne, $CH{\equiv}CCH_2CH_3$ _____ carbons   _____ hydrogens

6. If an alkyne has *n* carbon atoms and one triple bond, how many hydrogen atoms will it have?

_____

7. Look carefully at the ball-and-stick models and space-filling models of ethane, ethene, and ethyne. Describe the spatial arrangement of the atoms in each molecule.

_____

_____

_____

MATH SKILLS TRANSPARENCY MASTER   (36)

Hydrocarbon Density

Use with Chapter 21,
Section 21.3

Densities of Hydrocarbons (g/mL at 20°C)

Alkanes	Density	Alkenes	Density	Alkynes	Density
$CH_3(CH_2)_3CH_3$	0.626	$CH_2=CH(CH_2)_2CH_3$	0.641	$CH\equiv C(CH_2)_2CH_3$	0.690
$CH_3(CH_2)_4CH_3$	0.660	$CH_2=CH(CH_2)_3CH_3$	0.673	$CH\equiv C(CH_2)_3CH_3$	0.716
$CH_3(CH_2)_5CH_3$	0.684	$CH_2=CH(CH_2)_4CH_3$	0.697	$CH\equiv C(CH_2)_4CH_3$	0.733
$CH_3(CH_2)_6CH_3$	0.703	$CH_2=CH(CH_2)_5CH_3$	0.715	$CH\equiv C(CH_2)_5CH_3$	0.746
$CH_3(CH_2)_7CH_3$	0.718	$CH_2=CH(CH_2)_6CH_3$	0.730	$CH\equiv C(CH_2)_6CH_3$	0.757
$CH_3(CH_2)_8CH_3$	0.730	$CH_2=CH(CH_2)_7CH_3$	0.741	$CH\equiv C(CH_2)_7CH_3$	0.766
$CH_3(CH_2)_9CH_3$	0.740	$CH_2=CH(CH_2)_8CH_3$	0.750	$CH\equiv C(CH_2)_8CH_3$	0.773

MATH SKILLS TRANSPARENCY WORKSHEET **36**

Hydrocarbon Density

**Use with Chapter 21,
Section 21.3**

1. Describe the relationship between the number of carbon atoms and the density of hydrocarbons.

   _____

2. How does density vary among alkanes, alkenes, and alkynes with the same number of carbon atoms?

   _____

3. On the grid below, plot the density of each series of hydrocarbons versus the number of carbon atoms. Connect the data points for each series with a smooth curve. Label all three curves and both axes.

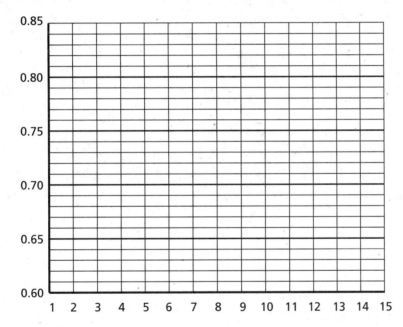

4. Use the curves that you drew to predict the density of the following 12-carbon hydrocarbons.

   $CH_3(CH_2)_{10}CH_3$ _____

   $CH_2 = CH(CH_2)_9CH_3$ _____

   $CH \equiv C(CH_2)_9CH_3$ _____

5. Suppose you were asked to predict the density of a straight-chain hydrocarbon with 15 carbon atoms. Would you have as much confidence in your prediction as you do for your prediction about 12-carbon hydrocarbons? Explain why or why not.

   _____

   _____

CHAPTER 21 STUDY GUIDE

Hydrocarbons

Section 21.1 Introduction to Hydrocarbons

In your textbook, read about natural sources of hydrocarbons and rating gasolines.

In the space at the left, write the word or phrase in parentheses that correctly completes the statement.

_____ **1.** (Petroleum, Natural gas) is a mixture of thousands of organic compounds.

_____ **2.** The boiling of petroleum and collection of its components is called (sedimentation, fractional distillation).

_____ **3.** In the process known as (cracking, knocking), heavier petroleum fractions are converted to gasoline by breaking their large molecules into smaller ones.

_____ **4.** A gasoline's ability to burn evenly and prevent knocking is expressed by its (hexane, octane) rating.

Use the diagram of a fractionation tower to answer the following questions.

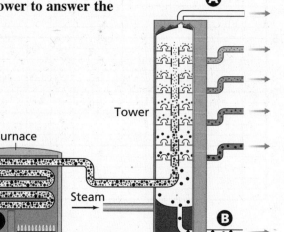

5. How does the temperature inside the tower vary from bottom to top?

_____

6. In what physical state is the material collected from pipe A? _____

7. What is the material collected from pipe A used for?

_____

8. What is the material collected from pipe B used for?

_____

9. Which pipe, A or B, collects hydrocarbons with higher boiling points? _____

10. Which pipe, A or B, collects smaller hydrocarbons? _____

Name ______________________ Date ____________ Class ____________

CHAPTER 21 **STUDY GUIDE**

Section 21.2 Alkanes

In your textbook, read about organic chemistry, hydrocarbons, and straight-chain alkanes.

Use each of the terms below just once to complete the passage.

homologous series	straight-chain alkanes

If all of the carbon atoms are linked by single covalent bonds and there are no branches, the compounds are called **(1)** ______________________. Ethane, propane, and butane are three examples. They are members of one **(2)** ______________________ because they differ from each other by a repeating unit (— CH_2 —).

In your textbook, read about branched-chain alkanes and naming them.

For each statement below, write *true* or *false*.

______________ **3.** The ability of carbon atoms to bond to two, three, or four other carbon atoms makes possible a variety of branched-chain alkanes.

______________ **4.** A carbon atom or group of carbon atoms that branch off the main hydrocarbon chain of an alkane is a substituent group.

______________ **5.** A skeletal formula is a way of representing an organic compound by showing only the hydrogen atoms.

Use the IUPAC rules to name the following structures.

6.
CH_3
|
$CH_2CH_2CH_2CH_2CH_2CH_2CH_3$

____

7.
CH_3
|
$CH_3CHCH_2CH_2CH_2CHCH_3$
|
CH_2
|
CH_3

____

Draw the structure of each of the following alkanes.

8. 2-methylheptane

9. 2,3,4-trimethylpentane

Section 21.2 *continued*

In your textbook, read about cycloalkanes.

For each item in Column A, write the letter of the matching item in Column B.

Column A	Column B

_____ **10.** A simplified way of representing an organic compound by showing only the carbon-carbon bonds

     a. *cyclo-*

_____ **11.** A way of representing an organic compound that saves space by not showing how the hydrogen atoms branch off the carbon atoms

     b. condensed structural formula

_____ **12.** Indicates that a hydrocarbon has a ring structure

     c. line structure

_____ **13.** A hydrocarbon that has a ring of carbon atoms in its structure

     d. cyclic hydrocarbon

Use the IUPAC rules to name the following structure.

14. CH_3

     _____

CH_2CH_3

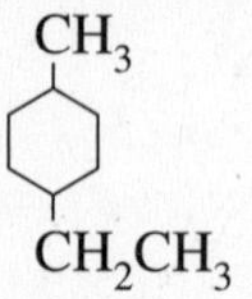

Draw the structure of the following cycloalkane.

15. 1-ethyl, 2-propylcyclobutane

In your textbook, read about the properties of alkanes and multiple carbon-carbon bonds.

In the space at the left, write the word or phrase in parentheses that correctly completes the statement.

_____ **16.** All the bonds in an alkane are (polar, nonpolar).

_____ **17.** The attractive forces between alkane molecules are (stronger, weaker) than the attractive forces between alkane and water molecules.

_____ **18.** Alkanes are (very, not very) soluble in water.

_____ **19.** The boiling points of alkanes (increase, decrease) with increasing molecular mass.

_____ **20.** The chief chemical property of alkanes is their (low, high) reactivity.

_____ **21.** Alkanes are often used as (solvents, fuels) because they readily undergo combustion in oxygen.

_____ **22.** Alkanes are (saturated, unsaturated) hydrocarbons because they have only single bonds.

CHAPTER (21)

STUDY GUIDE

Section 21.3 Alkenes and Alkynes

In your textbook, read about alkenes, alkynes, and naming alkynes.

Use the following words to complete the statements.

alkene	alkyne	electron density	ethene	ethyne

1. An _____ is a hydrocarbon that has one or more triple covalent bonds between carbon atoms.

2. The unsaturated hydrocarbon _____ is the starting material for the synthesis of the plastic polyethylene.

3. An _____ is a hydrocarbon that has one or more double covalent bonds between carbon atoms.

4. Torches used in welding burn _____, which is commonly called acetylene.

5. Alkenes and alkynes are more reactive than alkanes because double and triple bonds have

    greater _____ than single bonds have.

Circle the letter of the correct name for each of the following structures.

6. $CH_3CH_2CH{=}CHCH_2CH_2CH{=}CH_2$
    a. 1,5-octadiene
    b. 3,7-octadiene
    c. 4,8-dioctene

7. $CH_3CH_2C{\equiv}CCH_2CH_3$
    a. 3-hexene
    b. 3-hexyne
    c. 3-pentyne

Use the IUPAC rules to name the following structures.

8.
$$CH_3CH{=}CHCCH_3$$
with CH_3 above and CH_3 below the fourth carbon

_____

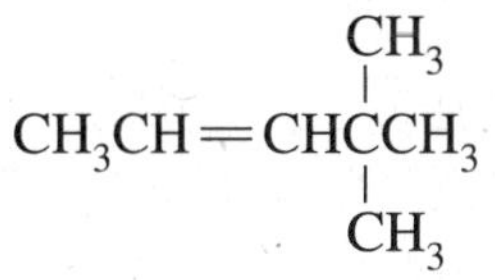

9.
a ring structure with $CH_2CH_2CH_2CH_3$

_____

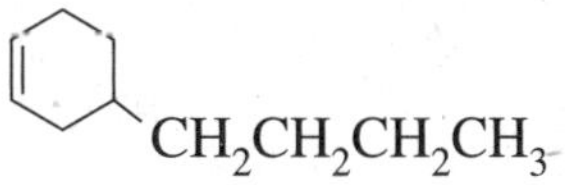

10.
$$CH_3CH_2CH_2CHCH_2C{\equiv}CCHCH_2CH_3$$
with CH_2CH_3 above and CH_2CH_3 below

_____

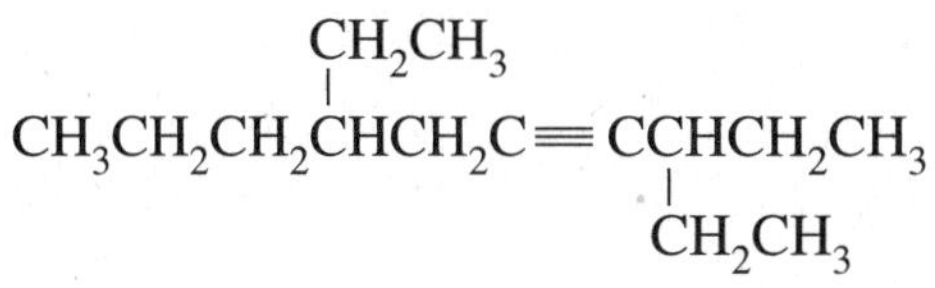

11.
$$CH_3CHCH_2CHCHCH_2CH{=}CHCH_3$$
with CH_3 and $CH_2CH_2CH_3$ above and CH_2CH_3 below

_____

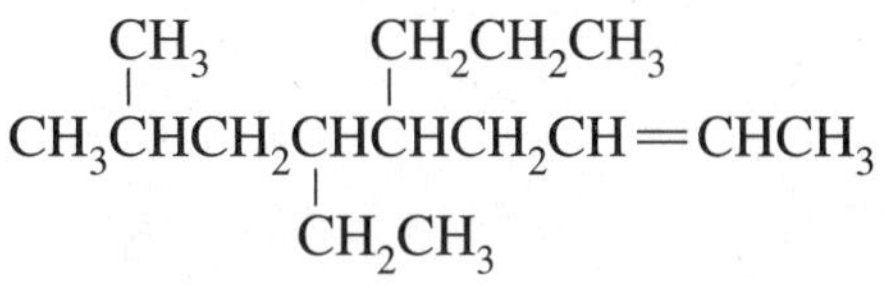

Name _____ Date _____ Class _____

CHAPTER 21 **STUDY GUIDE**

Section 21.4 Hydrocarbon Isomers

In your textbook, read about structural isomers, stereoisomers, chirality, and optical isomers.

Complete the concept map by writing the term below that fits the description at the right of each box.

chirality	geometric isomers	isomers	optical isomers
polarized light	stereoisomers	structural isomers	

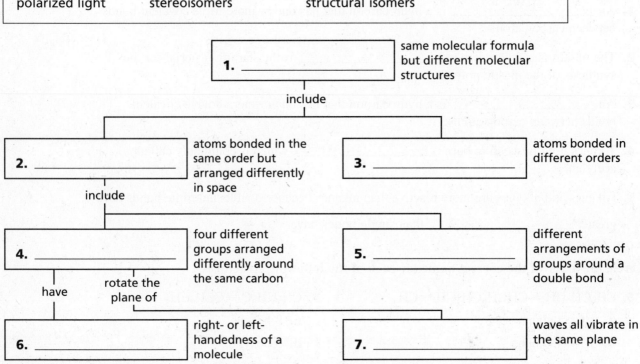

1. _____ same molecular formula but different molecular structures

include

2. _____ atoms bonded in the same order but arranged differently in space

3. _____ atoms bonded in different orders

include

4. _____ four different groups arranged differently around the same carbon

5. _____ different arrangements of groups around a double bond

have   rotate the plane of

6. _____ right- or left-handedness of a molecule

7. _____ waves all vibrate in the same plane

Identify the type of isomers represented by each of the following pairs of structures. Choose your answers from the following types: *geometric isomers, optical isomers, structural isomers.* (In item 8, the symbols W, X, Y, and Z represent hypothetical groups.)

8.
```
     X              Y
     |              |
 W — C — Y      W — C — X
     |              |
     Z              Z
```
_____

9.
```
  H        CH₂CH₃        H         H
   \      /               \       /
    C = C                  C = C
   /      \               /       \
CH₃CH₂    H          CH₂CH₃      CH₂CH₃
```
_____

10.
```
          CH₃
          |
CH₃CH₂CH₂CCH₃       CH₃CH₂CH₂CH₂CH₂CH₂CH₃
          |
          CH₃
```
_____

20   Chemistry: Matter and Change • Chapter 21   Study Guide

CHAPTER 21   **STUDY GUIDE**

Section 21.5 Aromatic Hydrocarbons

In your textbook, read about the structure of benzene and aromatic compounds.

Use the following words to complete the statements.

aliphatic compounds	aromatic compounds	carcinogens

1. Substances that cause cancer are called _____.

2. Alkanes, alkenes, and alkynes are examples of _____.

3. All _____ contain benzene rings as part of their structure.

Circle the letter of the choice that best completes the statement or answers the question.

4. What is the molecular formula of benzene?

   a. C_6H_6 **b.** C_6H_{12} **c.** C_6H_{14} **d.** $C_{12}H_{12}$

5. Which of the following is the best way to represent the structure of benzene?

   a.    **b.**    **c.**    **d.**

6. Compared to alkenes and alkynes of similar size, benzene is

   a. less reactive.   **c.** slightly more reactive.

   b. about as reactive.   **d.** much more reactive.

7. The electrons in the ring of an aromatic compound are

   a. held tightly by one carbon nucleus.

   b. localized between specific carbon nuclei.

   c. shared equally by all of the carbon nuclei.

   d. shared by only three of the carbon nuclei.

8. The use of aromatic compounds should be limited because many of them

   a. produce chimney soot.   **c.** have pleasant smells.

   b. can cause health problems.   **d.** cannot be synthesized.

Use the IUPAC rules to name the following structures.

9. 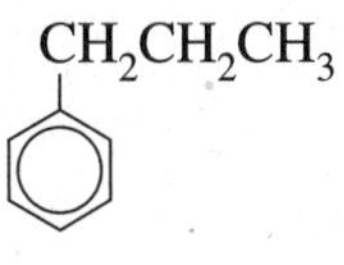 $CH_2CH_2CH_3$

10. 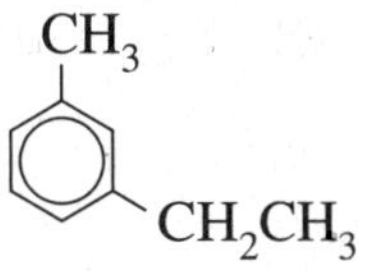 CH_3 CH_2CH_3

_____   _____

CHAPTER 21 CHAPTER ASSESSMENT

Hydrocarbons

Reviewing Vocabulary

In the space at the left, write the word or phrase in parentheses that correctly completes the statement.

_____ **1.** A hydrocarbon that has one or more triple covalent bonds between carbon atoms is called an (alkene, alkyne).

_____ **2.** All the carbon atoms are connected to each other by single bonds in (saturated, unsaturated) hydrocarbons.

_____ **3.** Isomers in which the atoms are bonded in different orders are known as (structural isomers, stereoisomers).

_____ **4.** (Geometric, Optical) isomers result from different arrangements of four different groups about the same carbon atom.

_____ **5.** (Straight-chain, Branched-chain) alkanes contain carbon atoms that are bonded to more than two other carbon atoms.

_____ **6.** Organic compounds that contain benzene rings are called (aromatic, aliphatic) compounds.

In the space at the left, write _true_ if the statement is true; if the statement is false, change the italicized word or phrase to make it true.

_____ **7.** All organic compounds contain the element _nitrogen_.

_____ **8.** Butane, pentane, and hexane are members of one _homologous series_.

_____ **9.** A _molecular_ formula shows the structure of a hydrocarbon but saves space by not showing how the hydrogen atoms branch off the carbon atoms.

_____ **10.** A carcinogen is a substance that causes _cancer_.

_____ **11.** Compounds that exist in right and left forms have a property called _chirality_.

_____ **12.** In the process called cracking, _lighter_ fractions of petroleum are converted into gasoline.

_____ **13.** Isomers have the same molecular formula but different _molecular structures_.

Understanding Main Ideas (Part A)

Circle the letter of the choice that best completes the statement.

1. Hydrocarbons contain only
   a. carbon.
   b. carbon and hydrogen.
   c. carbon, hydrogen, and oxygen.
   d. hydrogen and oxygen.

2. In a branched alkane, each branch attached to the main chain is called a(n)
   a. asymmetric carbon.
   b. cycloalkane.
   c. acetylene group.
   d. substituent group.

3. Cyclohexane is an example of
   a. a straight-chain alkane.
   b. a parent chain.
   c. a cyclic hydrocarbon.
   d. an alkene.

4. In polarized light, the light waves vibrate in
   a. one plane.
   b. two planes.
   c. three planes.
   d. all possible planes.

5. The boiling of petroleum to separate components is called
   a. cracking.
   b. knocking.
   c. fractional distillation.
   d. optical rotation.

Circle the letter of the correct name for each of the following structures.

6. $CH_3CH_2CH_2CH_2CH_3$
   a. propane
   b. pentane
   c. hexane

7. $CH_3CH=CHCH_2CH_3$
   a. 2-pentene
   b. 3-pentene
   c. 4-pentene

8. $CH_3CH_2C\equiv CCH_3$
   a. 4-pentyne
   b. 3-pentane
   c. 2-pentyne

Use the IUPAC rules to name the following structures.

9.
$$\begin{array}{c} CH_3 \\ | \\ CH_3CH_2CH_2CH_2CHCH_2CH_3 \end{array}$$

_____

10.
$$\begin{array}{c} CH_2CH_3 \\ | \\ CH_3CH=CHCHCH_2CH_2CH_3 \end{array}$$

_____

11. $CH_2CH_2CH_3$ ... CH_2CH_3

_____

_____

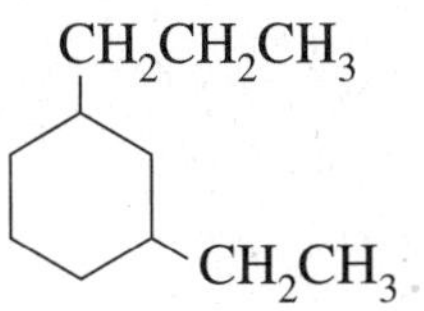

12. CH_3 ... CH_3

_____

_____

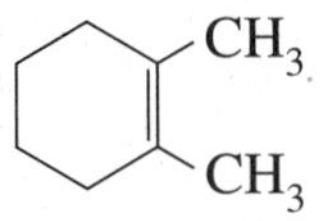

13. CH_2CH_3 ... CH_3CH_2 ... CH_2CH_3

_____

_____

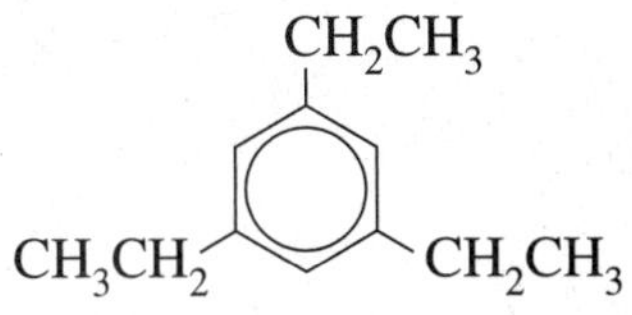

CHAPTER 21

Understanding Main Ideas (Part B)

Answer the following questions.

1. Why are there so many different organic compounds?

_____

_____

_____

_____

2. How does the sharing of electrons between carbon atoms in hexane differ from that in benzene?

_____

_____

_____

_____

Compare structures A, B, and C in each of the following groups. If B represents the same compound as A, write *same*. If B is an isomer of A, write the type of isomer (geometric, optical, or structural). Do the same for C.

3. $CH_3CH_2CH_2CHCH_3$ $CH_3CH_2CHCH_2CH_3$ $CH_3CHCH_2CH_2CH_3$

               CH_3 CH_3 CH_3

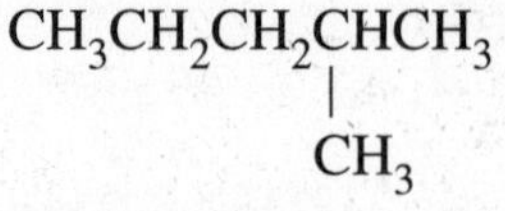

          A 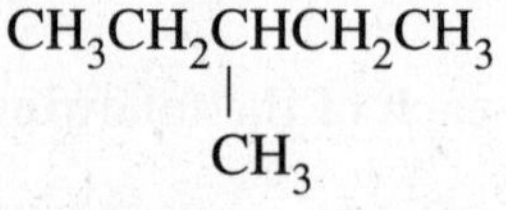   **B** 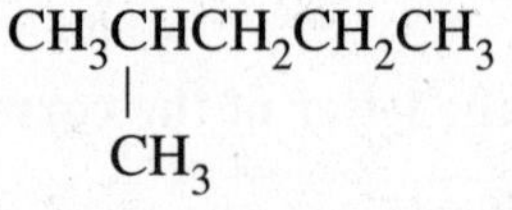 _____   **C** _____

4. CH_2CH_3 H CH_2CH_3

             |

$CH_3-\overset{|}{\underset{|}{C}}-H$ $CH_2CH_3-\overset{|}{\underset{|}{C}}-CH_2CH_2CH_3$ $CH_3-\overset{|}{\underset{|}{C}}-CH_2CH_2CH_3$

    $CH_2CH_2CH_3$ CH_3 H

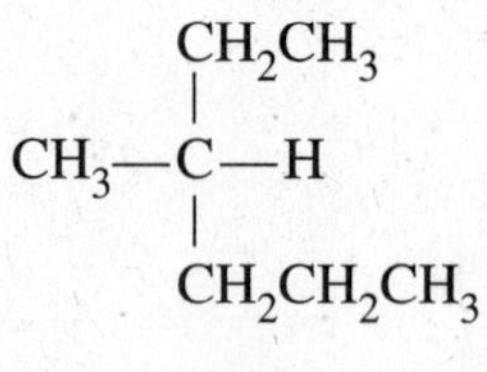

          A 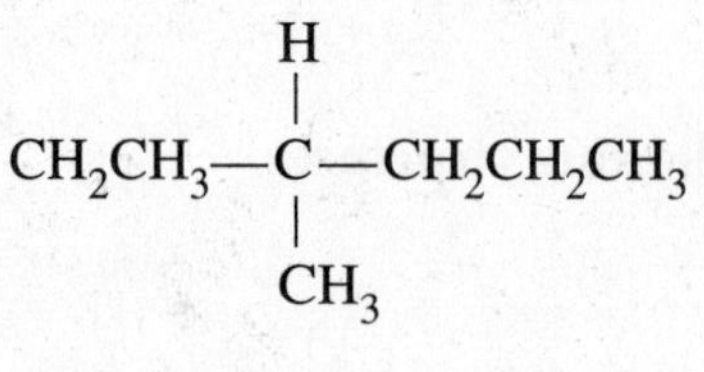   **B** 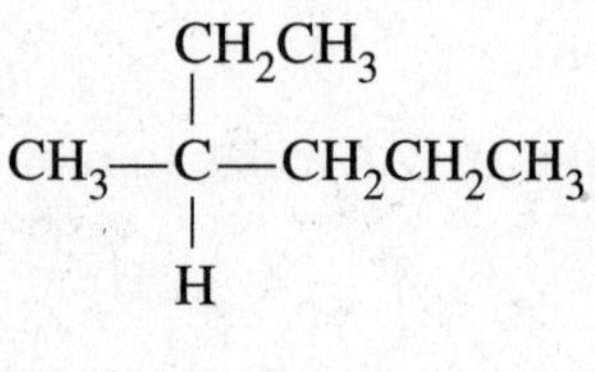 _____   **C** _____

5. $\underset{CH_3}{\overset{H}{>}}C=C\underset{H}{\overset{CH_3}{<}}$ $\underset{H}{\overset{CH_3}{>}}C=C\underset{CH_3}{\overset{H}{<}}$ $\underset{CH_3}{\overset{H}{>}}C=C\underset{CH_3}{\overset{H}{<}}$

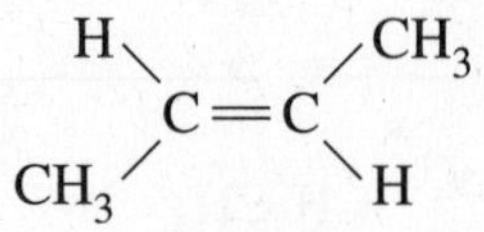

          A 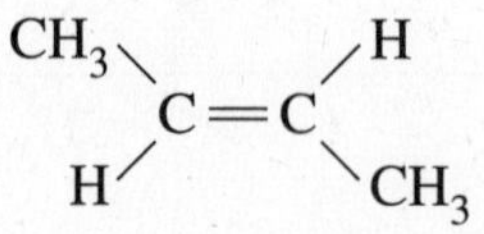   **B** 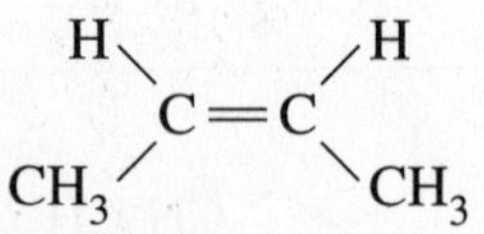 _____   **C** _____

CHAPTER 21 CHAPTER ASSESSMENT

Thinking Critically

Suppose a fractional distillation tower is set up to separate petroleum into four fractions. The boiling ranges of these fractions are shown in Table 1. The boiling points of several straight-chain alkanes are shown in Table 2 . Use the information in these tables to answer questions 1 and 2.

Table 1

Fraction	Boiling Range (°C)
1	below 40
2	40–100
3	101–275
4	above 275

Table 2

Name	Molecular Formula	Boiling Point (°C)
Methane	CH_4	−162
Propane	C_3H_8	−42
Pentane	C_5H_{12}	36
Hexane	C_6H_{14}	69
Heptane	C_7H_{16}	98
Octane	C_8H_{18}	126
Decane	$C_{10}H_{22}$	174
Pentadecane	$C_{15}H_{32}$	266
Hexadecane	$C_{16}H_{34}$	280

1. Which of the alkanes listed in Table 2 would you expect to find in each fraction?

   Fraction 1: _____   Fraction 3: _____

   Fraction 2: _____   Fraction 4: _____

2. In which fraction would you expect to find each of the following straight-chain alkanes, which are not listed in Table 2?

   nonane _____   ethane _____   icosane ($C_{20}H_{42}$) _____

Answer the following questions.

3. How many other geometric isomers are possible for the following compound? _____

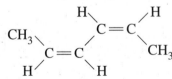

4. Would it be more difficult to distinguish between samples of two structural isomers or samples of two optical isomers? Explain.

   _____

   _____

   _____

   _____

CHAPTER 21

Applying Scientific Methods

A chemist is asked to analyze two samples of unknown compounds. The chemist performs a series of tests on the compounds to determine their molecular formula, solubility in water, and reactivity. The following table shows the results of these tests.

Sample	Molecular Formula	Solubility in Water	Reactivity
A	C_5H_{10}	low	low
B	C_5H_{10}	low	high

1. Do the tests show that A and B are the same compound or different compounds? Explain.

_____

_____

_____

To analyze the samples further, the chemist performs another test. This test indicates that one of the samples is a saturated hydrocarbon and the other sample is an unsaturated hydrocarbon.

2. Which sample is more likely to be the saturated hydrocarbon? Explain your reasoning.

_____

_____

_____

3. Draw the structure of one saturated hydrocarbon and one unsaturated hydrocarbon that have the molecular formula C_5H_{10}. (Hint: Remember that hydrocarbons can be straight-chain, branched-chain, or cyclic structures.) Name each compound, using the IUPAC rules.

4. List two other properties the chemist could test for to determine which specific compound is present in each sample.

_____

CHAPTER 21

CHAPTER ASSESSMENT

Applying Scientific Methods, *continued*

Benzene is an important hydrocarbon with many industrial uses. Almost all of the benzene produced in the United States comes from petroleum. However, the amount of benzene that is present in unrefined petroleum is very small. To produce benzene in the quantities that are needed, chemists convert other petroleum components into benzene through chemical reactions. A typical series of such reactions is shown below.

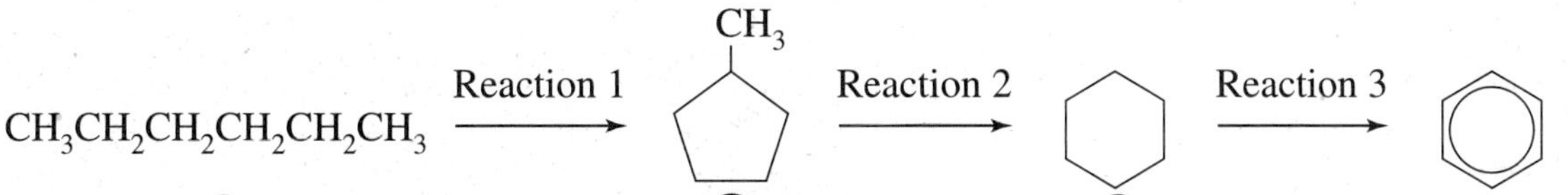

$CH_3CH_2CH_2CH_2CH_2CH_3$

A — Reaction 1 → **B** (CH₃ cyclopentane) — Reaction 2 → **C** (cyclohexane) — Reaction 3 → benzene

5. Use the IUPAC rules to name structures A–C.

A _____   **B** _____   **C** _____

6. How many carbon atoms or hydrogen atoms are added or lost in each reaction?

Reaction 1 _____

Reaction 2 _____

Reaction 3 _____

Benzene is widely used as a solvent in industry and in the organic chemistry laboratory. It is also a starting material in the manufacture of other aromatic compounds. Two such compounds are shown below.

CH_2CH_3 **D** CH_2CH_3 CH_3 **E**

7. Use the IUPAC rules to name structures D and E.

D _____   **E** _____

8. World War I brought an increased demand for benzene, which was used in the production of TNT and other explosives. That growth in demand led to the development of additional uses for benzene. Why do you think that increased production of a chemical such as benzene leads to the discovery of additional uses?

_____

_____

_____

_____

CHAPTER 21
Assessment

Student Recording Sheet

Standardized Test Practice

Multiple Choice

Select the best answer from the choices given, and fill in the corresponding circle.

1. Ⓐ Ⓑ Ⓒ Ⓓ
2. Ⓐ Ⓑ Ⓒ Ⓓ
3. Ⓐ Ⓑ Ⓒ Ⓓ

4. Ⓐ Ⓑ Ⓒ Ⓓ
5. Ⓐ Ⓑ Ⓒ Ⓓ
6. Ⓐ Ⓑ Ⓒ Ⓓ

7. Ⓐ Ⓑ Ⓒ Ⓓ
8. Ⓐ Ⓑ Ⓒ Ⓓ
9. Ⓐ Ⓑ Ⓒ Ⓓ

Short Answer

Answer each question with complete sentences.

10. _____

11. _____

12. _____

Extended Response

Answer each question with complete sentences.

13. _____

_____

_____

14. _____

_____

_____

SAT Subject Test: Chemistry

15. Ⓐ Ⓑ Ⓒ Ⓓ Ⓔ

16. Ⓐ Ⓑ Ⓒ Ⓓ Ⓔ

17. Ⓐ Ⓑ Ⓒ Ⓓ Ⓔ

Table of Contents

Chapter 22 Substituted Hydrocarbons and Their Reactions

miniLAB 22

Make an Ester

Observing and Inferring How can you recognize an ester?

Materials salicylic acid, methanol, distilled water, 10-mL graduated cylinder, Beral pipette, 250-mL beaker, concentrated sulfuric acid, top or bottom of a petri dish, cotton ball, small test tube, balance, weighing paper, hot plate, test-tube holder

Procedure

1. Read and complete the lab safety form.

2. Prepare a hot-water bath by pouring 150 mL of tap water into a 250-mL beaker. Place the beaker on a hot plate set at medium.

3. Use a balance and weighing paper to measure 1.5 g of salicylic acid. Place the salicylic acid in a small test tube and add 3 mL of distilled water. Use a 10-mL graduated cylinder to measure the water. Then add 3 mL of methanol. Use a Beral pipette to add 3 drops of concentrated sulfuric acid to the test tube. **WARNING:** *Concentrated sulfuric acid can cause burns. Methanol fumes are explosive—keep away from open flame. Handle chemicals with care.*

4. When the water is hot but not boiling, place the test tube in the bath for 5 minutes. Use a test tube clamp to remove the test tube from the bath and place in a test tube holder until needed.

5. Place the cotton ball in the petri dish half. Pour the contents of the test tube onto the cotton ball. Record your observation of the odor of the product.

Analysis

1. **Name** The common name of the ester that you produced is *oil of wintergreen*. Name some products that you think could contain the ester.

_____

_____

_____

2. **Evaluate** the advantages and disadvantages of using synthetic esters in consumer products as compared to using natural esters.

_____

_____

_____

_____

Internet: Observe Properties of Alcohols

Alcohols are organic compounds that contain the −OH functional group. How fast various alcohols evaporate indicates the strength of intermolecular forces in alcohols. The evaporation of a liquid is an endothermic process, absorbing energy from the surroundings. This means that the temperature will decrease as evaporation occurs.

Problem	**Objectives**	**Materials**	
How do intermolecular forces differ in three alcohols?	• **Measure** the rate of evaporation for water and several alcohols. • **Infer** the relative strength of intermolecular forces of alcohols from rate of evaporation data.	nonmercury thermometer stopwatch facial tissue cloth towel Beral pipettes (5) methanol	ethanol (95%) 2-propanol (99%) wire twist tie or small rubber band piece of cardboard for use as a fan

Safety Precautions

• **Always wear safety goggles and a lab apron.**
• **Alcohols are flammable. Keep them away from open flames.**

Pre-Lab

1. Read the entire **CHEMLAB.**

2. Prepare all written materials that you will take into the laboratory. Be sure to include safety precautions and procedure notes. Use the data table on the next page.

3. Draw structural formulas for the three alcohols you will use in this activity. Describe how the structures of these compounds are alike and how they are different.

_____

_____

_____

_____

4. What types of forces exist between these kinds of molecules? Suggest which alcohol may have the greatest intermolecular forces.

_____

_____

Procedure

1. Read and complete the lab safety form.

2. Prepare data tables for recording data.

3. Cut five 2-cm by 6-cm strips of tissue.

4. Place a thermometer on a folded towel lying on a flat table so that the bulb of the thermometer extends over the edge of the table. Make sure the thermometer cannot roll off the table.

5. Wrap a strip of tissue around the bulb of the thermometer. Secure the tissue with a wire twist tie placed above the bulb of the thermometer.

6. Choose one person to control the stopwatch and read the temperature on the thermometer. A second person will put a small amount of the liquid to be tested into a Beral pipette.

7. When both people are ready, squeeze enough liquid onto the tissue to completely saturate it. At the same time, the other person starts the stopwatch, reads the temperature, and records it in the data table.

8. Fan the tissue-covered thermometer bulb with a piece of cardboard or other stiff paper. After 1 min, read and record the final temperature in the data table. Remove the tissue and wipe the bulb dry.

9. Repeat steps 5 through 8 for each of the three alcohols: methanol, ethanol, and 2-propanol.

10. Obtain the classroom temperature and humidity data from your teacher.

11. **Cleanup and Disposal** Place the used tissues in the trash. Pipettes can be reused.

Evaporation Data			
Substance	**Starting temp (°C)**	**Temp after 1 minute (°C)**	**ΔT (°C)**
Water			
Methanol			
Ethanol			
2-Propanol			
Other alcohol			

Analyze and Conclude

1. **Observe and Infer** What can you conclude about the relationship between heat transfer and the differences in the temperature changes you observed?

_____

_____

2. **Evaluate** Molar enthalpies of vaporization (kJ/mol) for the three alcohols at 25°C are: methanol, 37.4; ethanol, 42.3; and 2-propanol, 45.4. What can you conclude about the relative strength of intermolecular forces existing in the three alcohols?

_____

_____

3. **Compare** Make a general statement comparing the molecular size of an alcohol in terms of the number of carbons in the carbon chain to the rate of evaporation of that alcohol.

_____

_____

CHEMLAB 22

4. **Observe and Infer** Post your data on the Internet at **glencoe.com**. Infer why there are differences between your data and those of other students.

_____

_____

5. **Error Analysis** Determine where errors might have been introduced in your procedure.

_____

_____

Inquiry Extension

Design an Experiment Suggest a way to make this experiment more quantitative and controlled. Design an experiment using your new method.

_____

_____

_____

_____

_____

_____

_____

TEACHING TRANSPARENCY MASTER   **65**

Naming Halocarbons

Use with Chapter 22,
Section 22.1

```
    H        H
    |        |
H — C ——— C — H
    |        |
    H        Cl
```
A

```
    H        H
    |        |
Cl — C ——— C — H
    |        |
    Cl       H
```
B

```
    H        H
    |        |
H — C ——— C — Cl
    |        |
    H        Cl
```
C

```
    Cl       H
    |        |
H — C ——— C — Cl
    |        |
    H        H
```
D

```
       Cl
       |
       C
      /|\
   Br  |  H
       H
```
E

```
    Cl       Br
    |        |
H — C ——— C — H
    |        |
    H        H
```
F

```
    H     H    H    Cl
    |     |    |    |        H
H — C ——— C —— C —— C —— C — H
    |     |    |    |        |
    H     H    F    Br       H
```
G

H

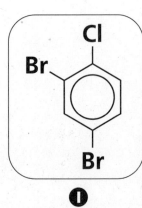

I

TEACHING TRANSPARENCY WORKSHEET **65**

Naming Halocarbons

**Use with Chapter 22,
Section 22.1**

1. What is the name for any non-carbon or non-hydrogen group, such as a halogen, that is present in an organic molecule and reacts in a certain way?

   _____

2. What is the name for any halocarbon in which the halogen is covalently bonded to an aliphatic carbon atom?

   _____

3. What is the name of the compound labeled A? Would the movement of the chlorine atom to another position on the two-carbon chain create a different compound?

   _____

4. What is the name of compound B? Why are numbers necessary in naming it?

   _____

   _____

   _____

5. What is the name of compound C? Compare the name of compound C to that of compound B, and explain your answer.

   _____

   _____

6. What is the name of compound D? _____

7. What rule is followed in naming halocarbons that have two different types of halogens? How are the numbers assigned?

   _____

   _____

8. What is the name of compound E? _____

9. What is the name of compound F? _____

10. What is the name of compound G? _____

11. What is the name for any halocarbon in which the halogen is covalently bonded to a benzene ring or other aromatic group?

   _____

12. What is the name of compound H? _____

13. What is the name of compound I?

   _____

TEACHING TRANSPARENCY MASTER

66

Alcohols, Ethers, and Amines

Use with Chapter 22, Section 22.2

A

```
        H              H           H
        |              |           |
  H  —  C  —  O  —  C  —  C  —  H
        |              |           |
        H              H           H
```

B

```
                        H
        H       H       |
        |       |       N  —  H
  H  —  C  —  C  —  C
        |       |       |
        H       H       H
```

C

```
        H       H       H
        |       |       |
  H  —  C  —  C  —  C  —  O  —  H
        |       |       |
        H       H       H
```

D

```
                                H
        H       H       H       |
        |       |       |       N  —  H
        N  —  C  —  C  —  C  —  H
        |       |       |       |
        H       H       H       H
```

E

```
        H       H       H
        |       |       |
  H  —  C  —  C  —  C  —  H
        |       |       |
  H  —  O       H       O  —  H
```

TEACHING TRANSPARENCY WORKSHEET **66**

Alcohols, Ethers, and Amines

**Use with Chapter 22,
Section 22.2**

1. What are the name and formula of the functional group in alcohols?

_____

2. With what suffix do the names of alcohols end?

_____

3. How is the position of the functional group indicated in naming alcohols?

_____

4. What structure is characteristic of ether molecules?

_____

5. In naming ethers, what rule is applied if an ether's alkyl groups are different?

_____

6. What structure is characteristic of amine molecules?

_____

7. Name the compounds labeled A–E.

compound A _____

compound B _____

compound C _____

compound D _____

compound E _____

8. Of compounds A, B, and C, which is likely to be a weak base?

_____

9. Of compounds A, B, and C, which is likely to have the lowest boiling point?

_____

10. Of compounds A, B, and C, which is most likely to have an offensive odor?

_____

Name ____________________ Date ____________ Class ____________

TEACHING TRANSPARENCY MASTER 67

Carbonyl, Carboxyl, and Amide Groups

Use with Chapter 22, Section 22.3

A

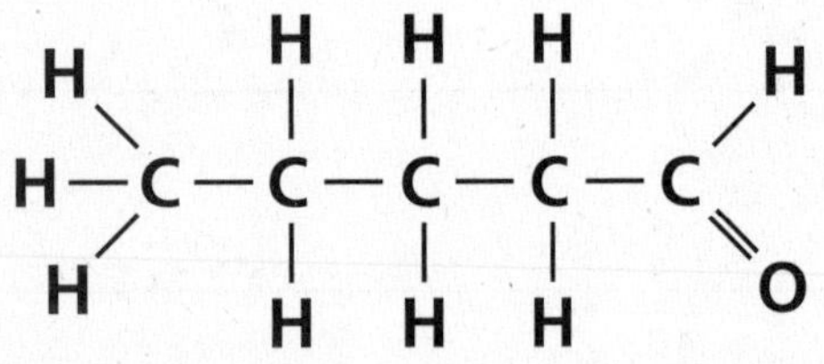

B

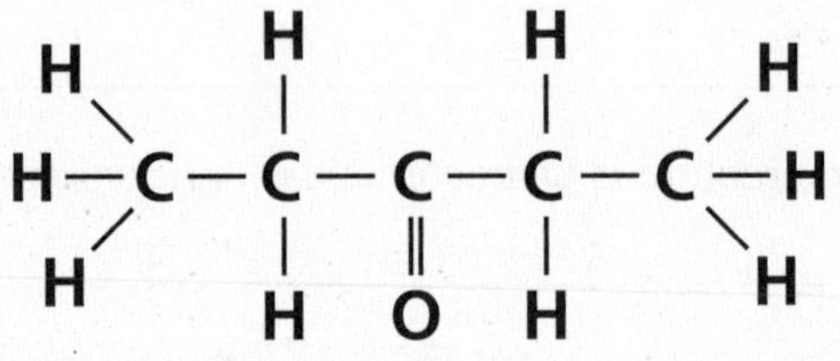

C

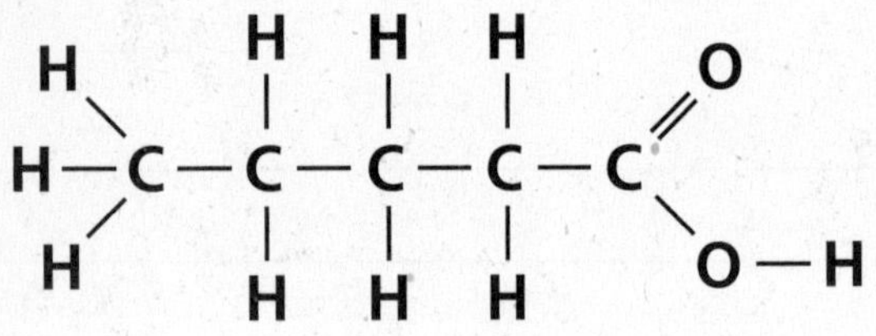

D

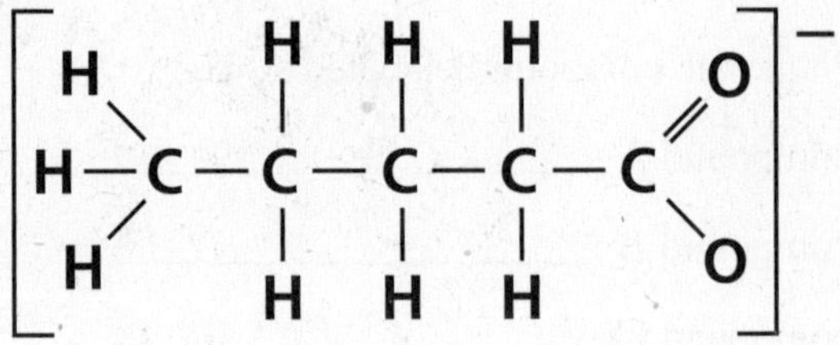

E

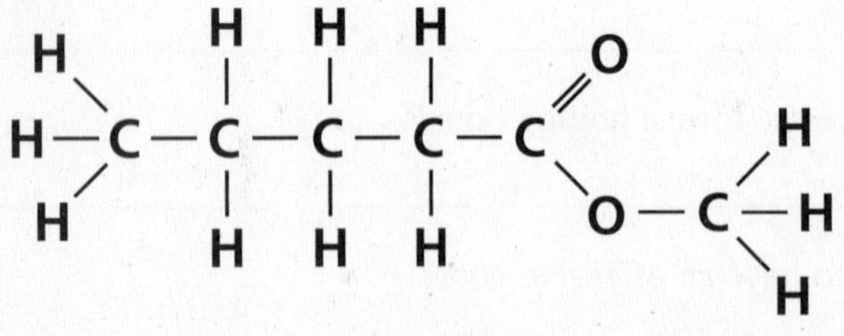

F

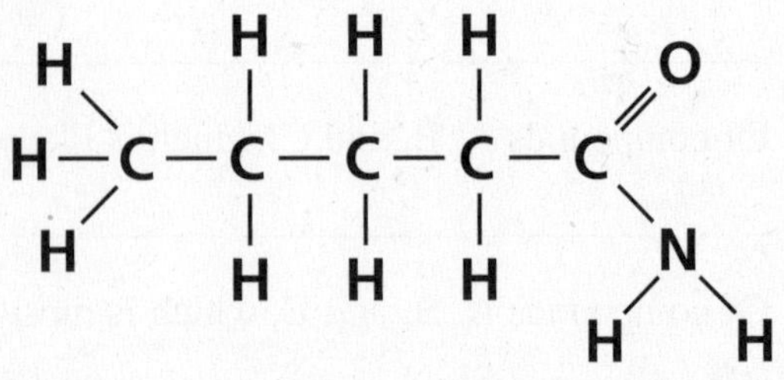

TEACHING TRANSPARENCY WORKSHEET **67**

Carbonyl, Carboxyl, and Amide Groups

Use with Chapter 22, Section 22.3

1. What is the name of the functional structural group that all the compounds shown have in common? Describe that structure.

   _____

   _____

2. The following questions apply to the compound labeled A on the transparency.

   a. What is the name of the compound? _____

   b. To what category of organic compound (carboxylic acid, ketone, ester, amide, or

   aldehyde) does it belong? _____

   c. State whether you would expect this compound to be polar and whether it can form hydrogen bonds with water. Also, predict whether the compound's boiling point would be lower or higher than that of the alcohol with the same number of carbon atoms.

   _____

   _____

3. The following questions apply to the compound labeled B on the transparency.

   a. What is the name of the compound? _____

   b. To what category of organic compound does it belong? _____

   c. State whether you would expect this compound to be polar, and whether it can form hydrogen bonds with water.

   _____

4. The following questions apply to the compound labeled C on the transparency.

   a. What is the name of the compound? _____

   b. To what category of organic compound does it belong? _____

   c. What are the name and formula of the functional group of compounds in this category?

   _____

   d. State whether you would expect this compound to be polar, whether it would ionize in water, and what the color of litmus paper in the resulting solution would be.

   _____

   _____

5. What is the name of the ion labeled D? _____

6. What are the names of the compounds labeled E and F on the transparency?

   _____

TEACHING TRANSPARENCY MASTER

68

Kinds of Organic Reactions

**Use with Chapter 22,
Section 22.4**

A

$$H-\underset{\underset{I}{|}}{\overset{\overset{H}{|}}{C}}-\underset{\underset{I}{|}}{\overset{\overset{H}{|}}{C}}-H \rightarrow \underset{H}{\overset{H}{C}}=\underset{H}{\overset{H}{C}} + I-I$$

B

$$\underset{H}{\overset{H}{C}}=\underset{H}{\overset{H}{C}} + \underset{H}{\overset{}{O}}_{H} \rightarrow H-\overset{H}{\underset{H}{C}}-\overset{H}{\underset{O-H}{C}}-H$$

C

$$H-\overset{O}{\underset{O-H}{C}} + \underset{H}{\overset{H}{O}}-\overset{H}{\underset{H}{C}}-H \rightarrow H-\overset{O}{\underset{O-\underset{H}{\overset{H}{C}}-H}{C}} + \underset{H}{\overset{O}{}}_{H}$$

D

$$H-\overset{H}{\underset{H}{C}}-\overset{H}{\underset{H}{C}}-H \rightarrow \underset{H}{\overset{H}{C}}=\underset{H}{\overset{H}{C}} + H-H$$

E

$$\overset{H}{\underset{H\,\,H}{\overset{|}{C}}}-Cl + [O-H]^- \rightarrow \overset{H}{\underset{H\,\,H}{\overset{|}{C}}}-O-H + Cl^-$$

F

$$\underset{H}{\overset{H}{C}}=\underset{H}{\overset{H}{C}} + H-H \rightarrow H-\overset{H}{\underset{H}{C}}-\overset{H}{\underset{H}{C}}-H$$

G

$$\underset{H}{\overset{H}{C}}=\underset{H}{\overset{H}{C}} + F-F \rightarrow H-\overset{F}{\underset{H}{C}}-\overset{F}{\underset{H}{C}}-H$$

H

$$H-\overset{H}{\underset{H}{C}}-\overset{H}{\underset{O-H}{C}}-H \rightarrow \underset{H}{\overset{H}{C}}=\underset{H}{\overset{H}{C}} + \underset{H}{\overset{O}{}}_{H}$$

I

$$\overset{H}{\underset{H\,\,H}{\overset{|}{C}}}_{H} + Br-Br \rightarrow \overset{H}{\underset{H\,\,Br}{\overset{|}{C}}}_{H} + H-Br$$

TEACHING TRANSPARENCY WORKSHEET (68)

Kinds of Organic Reactions

**Use with Chapter 22,
Section 22.4**

1. What is the name for the category of reaction in which one atom or a group of atoms in a molecule is replaced by another?

_____

2. Which two of the reactions labeled A–I are examples of that type of reaction?

_____

3. Which of these two reactions is also a halogenation reaction?

_____

4. What is the name for the category of reaction in which atoms on two adjacent carbon atoms are removed, forming an additional bond between the carbon atoms?

_____

5. Which three of the reactions labeled A–I are examples of that type of reaction?

_____

6. Which of these three reactions is also a dehydration reaction?

_____

7. Which of these three reactions is also a dehydrogenation reaction?

_____

8. What is the name for the category of reaction in which other atoms bond to each of two double-bonded or triple-bonded atoms?

_____

9. Which three of the reactions labeled A–I are examples of that type of reaction?

_____

10. Which of these three reactions is also a hydration reaction?

_____

11. Which of these three reactions is also a hydrogenation reaction?

_____

12. What is the name for the category of reaction in which two smaller organic molecules combine to form a more complex molecule, accompanied by the loss of a small molecule such as water?

_____

13. Which of the reactions labeled A–I is an example of that type of reaction?

_____

TEACHING TRANSPARENCY MASTER

69

Forming Polymers

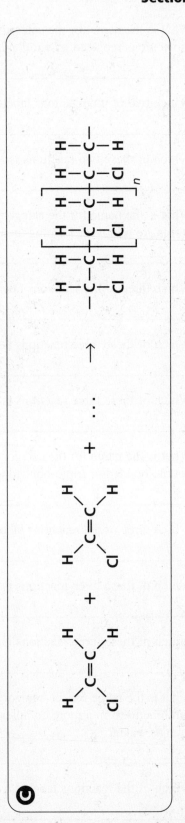

Name _____ Date _____ Class _____

Forming Polymers

**Use with Chapter 22,
Section 22.5**

1. Define the following terms.

a. polymer

_____

b. monomer

_____

c. structural unit of a polymer

_____

2. Look at the reaction labeled A, which illustrates a polymerization reaction.

a. What are the name and formula of the monomer? _____

b. What does the structure labeled *n* in reaction A represent?

_____

c. What is the name of the polymer produced? _____

d. What kind of polymerization reaction is reaction A: condensation or addition? How
can you tell?

_____

3. Look at polymerization reaction B.

a. The first of the monomers shown is called methyl terephthalate. What is the name of
the second monomer?

_____

b. What does the structure labeled *n* in reaction B represent?

_____

c. The name of the polymer produced in reaction B is poly(ethylene terephthalate). It is
commonly known as Dacron. What is the name of the other product formed?

_____

d. What kind of polymerization reaction is reaction B: condensation or addition? How
can you tell?

_____

4. Look at polymerization reaction C.

a. The monomer is commonly called vinyl chloride. What is its more formal
chemical name?

_____

b. The common abbreviated name of the polymer produced in reaction C is PVC. Of
what complete name is PVC an abbreviation?

_____

MATH SKILLS TRANSPARENCY MASTER 37

Naming Organic Compounds

Use with Chapter 22,
Section 22.1

Prefix	Number of Atoms or Functional Groups
hexa-	6
hepta-	7
octa-	8
nona-	9
deca-	10

Prefix	Number of Atoms or Functional Groups
(none)	1
di-	2
tri-	3
tetra-	4
penta-	5

MATH SKILLS TRANSPARENCY WORKSHEET (37)

Naming Organic Compounds

Use with Chapter 22,
Section 22.1

The table shows the prefixes used in naming functional groups such as those found in alkyl halides. Each prefix corresponds to the number of atoms or functional groups.

1. How many chlorine atoms are there in a molecule of 1,1-dibromo-2,3,3-trichloro-2,4,5,6-

tetraiodohexane? _____

   a. How many bromine atoms are there in that molecule? _____

   b. How many iodine atoms are there in the molecule? _____

   c. Find the total number of halogen atoms in the molecule. _____

   d. How many carbon atoms are there in the molecule? _____

   e. Given what you know about bonding in alkanes and substituted alkanes, find
   the number of hydrogen atoms in the molecule. Explain your reasoning.

   _____

   _____

   _____

2. How many fluorine atoms are there in a molecule of 1,2-difluoro-3,5,6-triiodobenzene? _____

   a. How many iodine atoms are there in that molecule? _____

   b. Find the total number of halogen atoms in the molecule. _____

   c. How many carbon atoms are there in the molecule? Explain.

   _____

   d. Given what you know about bonding in substituted aryl compounds, find the
   number of hydrogen atoms in the molecule. Explain your reasoning.

   _____

   _____

   _____

3. Use the table of prefixes to figure out the names of the compounds labeled *A, B, C,* and
D. Remember to use numerals to indicate the positions of the halogen atoms in the
molecules. Keep in mind that the halogens must be listed alphabetically and that the numbers are assigned so as to be as low as possible for the first halogen listed.

   a. compound A _____

   b. compound B _____

   c. compound C _____

   d. compound D _____

MATH SKILLS TRANSPARENCY MASTER　　　　(38)

Using *n* to Calculate Molecular Masses of Polymers

Use with Chapter 22, Section 22.5

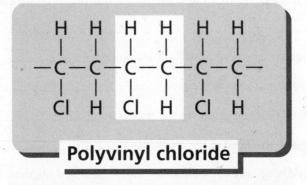

Polyvinyl chloride

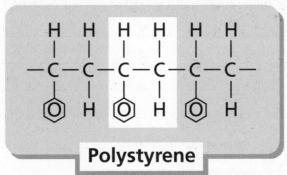

Polystyrene

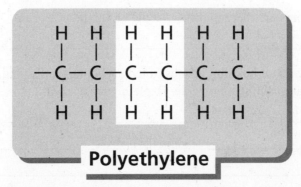

Polyethylene

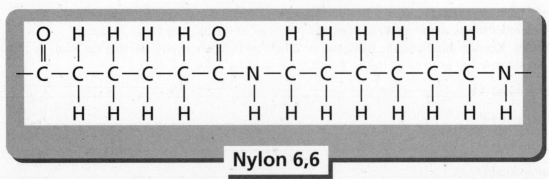

Nylon 6,6

MATH SKILLS TRANSPARENCY WORKSHEET   **38**

Using *n* to Calculate Molecular Masses of Polymers

Use with Chapter 22, Section 22.5

1. In general, what is the structural unit of a polymer?

_____

2. What does the letter *n* symbolize when used in reference to a polymer chain?

_____

3. How can the value of *n* be used to calculate the approximate molecular mass of a polymer, given a table of atomic masses and knowledge of the structural unit of the polymer?

_____

_____

4. Look at the polyvinyl chloride chain on the transparency. Its structural unit is shown in brackets. What is the mass of the structural unit? (Assume the following approximate atomic masses: H = 1.0 amu, C = 12.0 amu, Cl = 35.5 amu.)

_____

5. What is the approximate molecular mass of a polyvinyl chloride chain with 700 structural units?

_____

6. What is the mass of the structural unit of polystyrene?

_____

7. What is the approximate molecular mass of a polystyrene chain with 1250 structural units?

_____

8. What is the mass of the structural unit of polyethylene?

_____

9. What is the approximate molecular mass of a polyethylene chain with 900 structural units?

_____

10. What is the mass of the structural unit of nylon 6,6? (Assume the following atomic masses: O = 16.0 amu, N = 14.0 amu.)

_____

_____

11. What is the approximate molecular mass of a nylon 6,6 chain with 1750 structural units?

_____

Substituted Hydrocarbons and Their Reactions

Section 22.1 Alkyl Halides and Aryl Halides

In your textbook, read about functional groups.

Circle the letter of the choice that best completes the statement or answers the question.

1. In hydrocarbons, carbon atoms are generally linked to
   a. other carbon atoms only.   **c.** both carbon and hydrogen atoms.
   b. hydrogen atoms only.   **d.** atoms of any element.

2. Which of the following is an element commonly found in organic compounds?
   a. nitrogen   **b.** argon   **c.** cesium   **d.** calcium

3. Atoms or groups of atoms, other than hydrogen and carbon, that occur in organic molecules and react in a certain way are called
   a. functional groups.   **b.** polymers.   **c.** radicals.   **d.** monomers.

4. Which of the following is NOT a functional group?
   a. a double bond   **b.** a triple bond   **c.** an alkane chain   **d.** a chlorine atom

In your textbook, read about organic compounds containing halogens.

Use each of the terms below just once to complete the passage.

| alkyl halide | aryl halide | benzene | chiral | halocarbon | optical isomer |

Any organic compound containing a fluorine, chlorine, bromine, or iodine substituent is

called a(n) **(5)**_____. Such a compound in which the substituent replaces a

hydrogen in a hydrocarbon containing only single bonds is called a(n)

(6)_____. If the substituent replaces a hydrogen bonded to an aromatic

compound such as **(7)**_____, the resulting compound is called a(n)

(8)_____. If an organic compound contains four different groups attached

to the same carbon atom, the compound is referred to as a(n) **(9)**_____. In

that case, the carbon atom is called a(n) **(10)**_____ carbon.

CHAPTER 22   **STUDY GUIDE**

Section 22.2 **Alcohols, Amines, and Ethers**

In your textbook, read about the structure and properties of alcohols.

Circle the letter of the choice that best completes the statement or answers the question.

1. An alcohol is an organic compound in which a hydrogen atom of a hydrocarbon has been replaced by
   a. a hydroxyl group.   **b.** an oxygen atom.   **c.** an NH_2 group.   **d.** a COOH group.

2. Which of the following suffixes is used in naming alcohols?
   a. *-al*   **b.** *-oic*   **c.** *-ol*   **d.** *-ane*

3. The alcohol produced commercially in largest quantity is
   a. methanol.   **b.** isopropyl.   **c.** ether.   **d.** ethanol.

4. Alcohol molecules are generally
   a. nonpolar.   **b.** ionic.   **c.** very slightly polar.   **d.** moderately polar.

5. The alcohol produced by yeasts is
   a. methanol.   **b.** ethanol.   **c.** isopropanol.   **d.** cyclohexanol.

6. The simplest alcohol is
   a. methanol.   **b.** ethanol.   **c.** isopropanol.   **d.** butanol.

7. A poisonous alcohol used as a solvent for certain plastics and in the manufacture of insecticides is
   a. butanol.   **b.** ethanol.   **c.** cyclohexanol.   **d.** isopropanol.

8. Which of the following describes the solubility of ethanol in water?
   a. completely insoluble **b.** slightly soluble   **c.** immiscible   **d.** completely miscible

9. What intermolecular attraction gives alcohols many of their physical properties?
   a. London forces   **b.** hydrogen bonds   **c.** ionic forces   **d.** dipole-dipole forces

10. Denatured alcohol is
    a. a mixture of two alcohols.
    b. ethanol to which noxious solvents have been added.
    c. ethanol that has been distilled.
    d. ethanol diluted with water.

11. How is ethanol generally removed from a water solution?
    a. filtration   **b.** distillation   **c.** adsorption   **d.** precipitation

12. The position of the functional group in an alcohol is indicated in its name by a
    a. letter at the end.   **c.** number and dash at the end.
    b. letter at the beginning.   **d.** number and dash at the beginning.

Section 22.2 *continued*

In your textbook, read about the structure and properties of ethers and amines.

For each statement below, write *true* or *false*.

_____ **13.** An ether contains an oxygen atom bonded to two carbon atoms.

_____ **14.** Ethers generally have much lower boiling points than alcohols of the same size.

_____ **15.** Ethers generally are more soluble in water than are alcohols.

_____ **16.** Ether molecules form hydrogen bonds with each other.

_____ **17.** Amines contain nitrogen bonded to carbon.

_____ **18.** More than one amino group can be present in an amine molecule.

_____ **19.** Amines are typically acids.

_____ **20.** Volatile amines tend to have pleasant odors.

In your textbook, read about naming alcohols, amines, and ethers.

Match each of the lettered structures (a–l) to the following names.

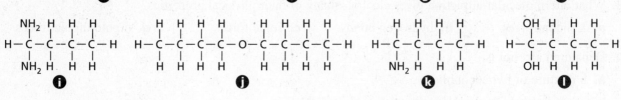

_____ **21.** 1-butanol

_____ **22.** 2-butanol

_____ **23.** 1,1-butanediol

_____ **24.** 2,2-butanediol

_____ **25.** 1,2-butanediol

_____ **26.** butyl ether

_____ **27.** butylpropyl ether

_____ **28.** 1-butylamine

_____ **29.** 2-butylamine

_____ **30.** 1,1-butyldiamine

_____ **31.** 2,2-butyldiamine

_____ **32.** 1,2-butyldiamine

STUDY GUIDE

Section 22.3 Carbonyl Compounds

In your textbook, read about aldehydes and ketones.

Circle the letter of the choice that best completes the statement or answers the question.

1. In a carbonyl group, an oxygen atom is

   a. single-bonded to a carbon atom.

   b. double-bonded to a carbon atom.

   c. bonded to a hydrogen atom.

   d. bonded to a carbon atom and another oxygen atom.

2. Which of the following makes a compound a ketone?

   a. a carboxyl group at the end

   b. a carboxyl group between carbon atoms

   c. a carbonyl group at the end

   d. a carbonyl group between carbon atoms

3. The formal names of aldehydes end with the suffix

   a. *-one.*   **b.** *-al.*   **c.** *-oic.*   **d.** *-ane.*

4. Which of the following correctly expresses the order of solubility, from greatest to least, of aldehydes, alcohols, and alkanes?

   a. aldehydes, then alkanes, then alcohols

   b. aldehydes, then alcohols, then alkanes

   c. alcohols, then aldehydes, then alkanes

   d. alcohols, then alkanes, then aldehydes

5. Which of the following is true of ketones in comparison to aldehydes?

   a. Neither is polar, and they are equally reactive.

   b. Ketones are polar, but aldehydes are not, and ketones are less reactive.

   c. Both are polar, and ketones are more reactive.

   d. Both are polar, and ketones are less reactive.

In your textbook, read about carboxylic acids, esters, and amides.

Use each of the terms below just once to complete the passage.

amide	carboxyl	carboxylic acids	ester	*-oic*	proteins

The COOH group is called a(n) **(6)** _____. That group is found in the organic

compounds called **(7)** _____. The formal name of such compounds is formed by

adding the suffix **(8)** _____ to the corresponding alkane, followed by the word

acid. A(n) **(9)** _____ is a compound in which the acidic hydrogen of an organic

acid is replaced by a carbon atom or hydrocarbon chain. A(n) **(10)** _____ is a

compound in which the –OH group of an organic acid is replaced by a nitrogen atom bonded to

other atoms. The functional group of such compounds is found in **(11)** _____.

Section 22.4 **Other Reactions of Organic Compounds**

In your textbook, read about categories of organic reactions.

Match the descriptions of reactions in Column A with the types of reactions in Column B.

Column A	Column B
_____ 1. An atom or a group of atoms is replaced by other atoms or groups.	**a.** elimination
_____ 2. An atom or a group of atoms is replaced by F, Cl, Br, or I.	**b.** dehydration
_____ 3. Additional bonds are formed between adjacent carbon atoms by the removal of atoms from the carbons.	**c.** condensation
_____ 4. H atoms are removed.	**d.** substitution
_____ 5. Atoms that form water are removed.	**e.** addition
_____ 6. Other atoms bond to carbons that are double or triple bonded.	**f.** dehydrogenation
_____ 7. Molecules join to form a larger molecule, with the loss of a small molecule.	**g.** halogenation

In your textbook, read about predicting the products of organic reactions.

Circle the letter of the choice that best answers the question.

8. What would be the products of a dehydration reaction in which ethanol was the reactant?

   a. ethyne and water   **b.** ethyne and hydrogen **c.** ethene and water   **d.** ethene and hydrogen

9. What would be the product of a hydrogenation reaction in which propene and hydrogen were the reactants?

   a. propyne   **b.** propane   **c.** propanol   **d.** propanal

10. Suppose that ethene and chlorine react to form 1,2-dichloroethane. What type of reaction would that be?

   a. addition   **b.** elimination   **c.** substitution   **d.** condensation

11. What kind of reaction is represented by the following equation, which contains structural formulas?

   a. addition

   b. elimination

   c. substitution

   d. condensation

$$H-\underset{\underset{H}{|}}{\overset{\overset{F}{|}}{C}}-\underset{\underset{H}{|}}{\overset{\overset{F}{|}}{C}}-H \rightarrow H-\overset{\overset{H}{|}}{C}=\overset{\overset{H}{|}}{C}-H + F-F$$

12. What kind of reaction occurs when an unsaturated fat is converted to a saturated fat?

   a. dehydrogenation   **b.** hydrogenation   **c.** dehydration   **d.** hydration

Section 22.5 Polymers

In your textbook, read about monomers and polymers.

Use each of the terms below just once to complete the passage.

addition	catalyst	cellulose	condensation	celluloid
monomer	polymer	water	polymerization	

A large molecule consisting of many repeating structural units is called a(n) **(1)**_____.

A reaction in which such a compound is produced is called a(n) **(2)**_____ reaction.

Each of the unit molecules from which such a large molecule is made is called a(n)

(3)_____. The natural polymer **(4)**_____, which is found in

wood fiber, was treated with nitric acid to produce the first plastic, **(5)**_____.

A substance called a(n) **(6)**_____ is often required to make a polymerization

proceed at a reasonable rate. In a(n) **(7)**_____ polymerization, all the atoms present

in the monomers are present in the product. In a(n) **(8)**_____ polymerization, the

product is formed with the loss of a small by-product, usually **(9)**_____.

In your textbook, read about polymerization and the properties of polymers.

For each statement below, write *true* or *false*.

_____ **10.** The repeating group of atoms formed by the bonding of monomers is
            called the structural unit of the polymer.

_____ **11.** The number of structural units in a polymer chain is represented by the letter n.

_____ **12.** Nylon is made by means of an addition polymerization.

_____ **13.** Polymers do not differ greatly in their properties.

_____ **14.** Thermosetting plastics are generally more difficult to recycle than are
            thermoplastic polymers.

_____ **15.** Most of the plastic waste produced in the United States is recycled.

Draw the following structure.

16. The monomer that reacts to make the polymer shown below

$$-CH_2-CH\left[CH_2-CH\right]_n CH_2-CH-$$
$$\quad\quad\;\; |\quad\quad\quad\;\; |\quad\quad\quad\;\; |$$
$$\quad\quad\; CH_3\quad\quad CH_3\quad\quad CH_3$$

CHAPTER 22 CHAPTER ASSESSMENT

Substituted Hydrocarbons and Their Reactions

Reviewing Vocabulary

Match the definition in Column A with the term in Column B.

Column A	Column B
_____ **1.** In an organic molecule, any atom or group of atoms that reacts in a certain way	**a.** ether
_____ **2.** Large molecule consisting of many repeating subunits	**b.** ketone
_____ **3.** Ethanol with small amounts of noxious materials added	**c.** functional group
_____ **4.** Compound containing a nitrogen atom bonded to a carbon atom in an aliphatic chain or aromatic ring	**d.** denatured alcohol
_____ **5.** Compound with a carbonyl group bonded to two carbon atoms	**e.** amide
_____ **6.** Compound in which the acidic hydrogen of a carboxyl group is replaced by a carbon atom	**f.** halocarbon
_____ **7.** A group in which a carbonyl group is bonded to a hydroxyl group	**g.** aldehyde
_____ **8.** Compound with an oxygen atom bonded to two carbon atoms	**h.** hydroxyl group
_____ **9.** Hydrogen and fluorine atoms bonded to carbon to produce a hydrofluorocarbon	**i.** carboxylic acid
_____ **10.** Compound containing a carbonyl group bonded to a carbon atom and to a hydrogen atom	**j.** amine
_____ **11.** Reaction in which all atoms in the monomer are in the polymer	**k.** polymer
_____ **12.** Reaction in which monomers with at least two functional groups combine to form a polymer, with the loss of a small by-product	**l.** carbonyl group
_____ **13.** Compound in which the −OH group of a carboxylic acid is replaced by a nitrogen atom bonded to other atoms	**m.** monomer
_____ **14.** An addition reaction in which a hydrogen atom and a hydroxyl group from a water molecule add to a double or triple bond	**n.** addition polymerization
_____ **15.** An −OH group	**o.** carboxyl group
_____ **16.** A group with an oxygen atom double-bonded to a carbon atom	**p.** ester
_____ **17.** Compound containing a carboxyl group	**q.** condensation polymerization
_____ **18.** A single unit molecule from which a polymer is made	**r.** HFC
_____ **19.** Organic compound containing fluorine, chlorine, bromine, or iodine	**s.** hydration reaction

Understanding Main Ideas (Part A)

Circle the letter of the choice that best completes the statement or answers the question.

1. In which kind of reaction is a combination of atoms removed from two adjacent carbon atoms, forming an additional bond between the carbon atoms?
   a. substitution　　**b.** elimination　　**c.** addition　　**d.** condensation

2. In which kind of reaction is an atom or group of atoms in a molecule replaced by another atom or group of atoms?
   a. substitution　　**b.** elimination　　**c.** addition　　**d.** condensation

3. Which of the following is an example of a thermosetting plastic?
   a. nylon　　**b.** polyethylene　　**c.** Bakelite　　**d.** none of the above

4. The simplest carboxylic acid is commonly known as
   a. acetic acid.　　**b.** acetone.　　**c.** formaldehyde.　　**d.** formic acid.

5. Which of the following tend to be basic?
   a. amides　　**b.** amines　　**c.** alcohols　　**d.** ethers

6. Which of the following is a type of addition reaction?
   a. hydrogenation　　**b.** dehydration　　**c.** dehydrogenation　　**d.** halogenation

In the space at the left, write *true* if the statement is true; if the statement is false, change the italicized term to make it true.

_____ **7.** The process called *cracking* breaks large alkanes from petroleum into smaller carbon compounds.

_____ **8.** *Esters* are often found in natural and artificial fragrances and flavors.

_____ **9.** A dehydration reaction releases *hydrogen*.

_____ **10.** Ethers tend to have *lower* boiling points than do alcohols of similar size and mass.

_____ **11.** The names of ketones end with the suffix *-ane*.

_____ **12.** The names of aldehydes end with the suffix *-ol*.

_____ **13.** Ketones tend to be *more* reactive than aldehydes.

_____ **14.** *Amide* groups are found repeated in proteins.

_____ **15.** An alkene can be produced from an alkyl halide by means of an *elimination* reaction.

_____ **16.** Nylon is synthesized by means of *addition* polymerization.

_____ **17.** *A thermoplastic* is an organic compound containing a halogen atom bonded to a benzene ring or other aromatic group.

CHAPTER 22   **CHAPTER ASSESSMENT**

Understanding Main Ideas (Part B)

Use the illustration, which shows the structures of a number of molecules, to answer the following questions.

1a. Describe the structure of the functional group in molecule A.

_____

_____

b. What is the name for this category of compound? _____

c. What is the formal name of this compound? _____

2a. Describe the structure of the functional group in molecule B.

_____

b. What is the name for this category of compound? _____

c. What is the formal name of this compound? _____

3a. Describe the structure of the functional group in molecule C.

_____

_____

b. What is the name for this category of compound? _____

c. What is the formal name of this compound? _____

4a. Describe the structure of the functional group in molecule D.

_____

b. What is the name for this category of compound? _____

c. What is the formal name of this compound? _____

Thinking Critically

Use the reaction below to answer the following questions.

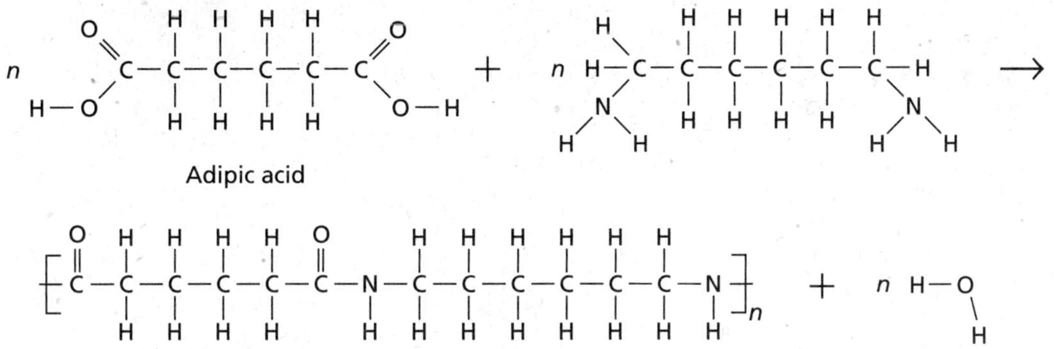

Adipic acid

1. The reaction shown is a polymerization reaction. What is a polymerization reaction?

_____

_____

2. One of the monomers in the above reaction is adipic acid. What category of compound is this substance? How can you tell?

_____

3. What does the term *structural unit of a polymer* mean?

_____

4. How is the structural unit of the polymer represented in the above reaction?

_____

5. The polymer produced is called nylon 6,6. What is the name for the functional group that has formed in the polymer product?

_____

6. What type of polymerization reaction is shown: an addition polymerization or a condensation polymerization? Explain.

_____

_____

7. What is the by-product of the reaction? _____

Applying Scientific Methods

Four unknown substituted hydrocarbons, W, X, Y, and Z, have been given to a chemistry student to identify. All of the compounds contain a chain of three carbon atoms per molecule. One of the unknowns is an alcohol, another an aldehyde, another an amine, and the remaining one a carboxylic acid. The student carries out various experiments to find out about some of the properties of each compound, which he will use to determine the identities of the compounds. The information he collects is summarized in the table below. Use the data to answer the questions that follow.

Property	Unknown W	Unknown X	Unknown Y	Unknown Z
Odor	Pungent, irritating	Pungent, sweet/medicinal	Sharp, sour	Ammonia-like
Boiling point (°C)	49	97	141	49
Solubility in water	Somewhat soluble	Completely miscible	Completely miscible	Somewhat soluble
Acidity in H$_2$O solution	Neutral	Neutral	Acidic	Basic

1. On the basis of the results of his acidity study, the student concludes that Y is the carboxylic acid. He claims to be unable to derive any further conclusions from the acidity tests. Comment on his conclusions.

   _____

   _____

   _____

   _____

   _____

   _____

2. The student examines the water-solubility data, but claims that it is not very useful in determining the identities of the compounds. Comment on the student's claim.

   _____

   _____

   _____

   _____

   _____

   _____

Applying Scientific Methods, *continued*

3. On the basis of the odor test, the student concludes that Z must be the amine, and that the test provides further confirmation that Y is the carboxylic acid. Comment on his conclusions.

_____

_____

_____

_____

4. On the basis of his findings so far, the student feels that he now needs only to identify W and X, one as the alcohol and the other as the aldehyde. On the basis of the results of the boiling-point test, the student concludes that X is the aldehyde and W the alcohol. Comment on his conclusions.

_____

_____

_____

_____

5. What is your own final conclusion as to the identity of each unknown?

_____

_____

_____

_____

6. What are the names of the compounds, as far as can be determined, given your answer to question 5 and the fact that each compound contains a chain of three carbon atoms?

_____

_____

_____

7. How do the student's overall procedure and your reasoning illustrate scientific methods?

_____

_____

_____

_____

_____

CHAPTER 22
Assessment Student Recording Sheet

Standardized Test Practice

Multiple Choice

Select the best answer from the choices given, and fill in the corresponding circle.

1. Ⓐ Ⓑ Ⓒ Ⓓ   4. Ⓐ Ⓑ Ⓒ Ⓓ   7. Ⓐ Ⓑ Ⓒ Ⓓ   10. Ⓐ Ⓑ Ⓒ Ⓓ

2. Ⓐ Ⓑ Ⓒ Ⓓ   5. Ⓐ Ⓑ Ⓒ Ⓓ   8. Ⓐ Ⓑ Ⓒ Ⓓ   11. Ⓐ Ⓑ Ⓒ Ⓓ

3. Ⓐ Ⓑ Ⓒ Ⓓ   6. Ⓐ Ⓑ Ⓒ Ⓓ   9. Ⓐ Ⓑ Ⓒ Ⓓ

Short Answer

Answer each question with complete sentences.

12. _____

13. _____

Extended Response

Answer each question with complete sentences.

14. _____

_____

_____

15. _____

_____

_____

SAT Subject Test: Chemistry

16. Ⓐ Ⓑ Ⓒ Ⓓ Ⓔ   17. Ⓐ Ⓑ Ⓒ Ⓓ Ⓔ   18. Ⓐ Ⓑ Ⓒ Ⓓ Ⓔ

Table of Contents

Chapter 23 The Chemistry of Life

miniLAB 23
Observe a Saponification Reaction

Applying Concepts How is soap made? The reaction between a triglyceride and a strong base such as sodium hydroxide is called saponification. A sample chemical reaction is shown in Figure 23.16.

Materials solid vegetable shortening, 250-mL beaker, 600-mL beaker, 6.0*M* NaOH, ethanol, saturated NaCl solution, stirring rod, hot plate, tongs, 25-mL graduated cylinder, evaporating dish, cheesecloth (20 cm × 20 cm), funnel

Procedure

1. Read and complete the lab safety form.
2. Place a 250-mL beaker on the hot plate. Add 25 g solid vegetable shortening to the beaker. Turn the hot plate on at a medium setting.
3. As the vegetable shortening melts, use a 25-mL graduated cylinder to slowly add 12 mL ethanol and then 5 mL 6.0*M* NaOH to the beaker. **WARNING:** *Ethanol is flammable. NaOH causes skin burns. Wear gloves.*
4. Heat the mixture for about 15 min. Use a stirring rod to occasionally stir the mixture. Do not allow it to boil.
5. When the mixture begins to thicken, use tongs to remove the beaker from the heat. Allow the beaker to cool for 5 min, then place it in a cold water bath in a 600-mL beaker.
6. Add 25 mL saturated NaCl solution to the mixture in the beaker. The soap is not very soluble and will appear as small clumps.
7. Collect the solid soap clumps by filtering them through a cheesecloth-lined funnel.
8. Using gloved hands, press the soap into an evaporating dish. Remove your gloves and wash your hands.

Analysis

1. **Explain** What type of bonds present in the triglycerides are broken during the saponification reaction?

_____

_____

2. **Identify** the type of salt formed in this chemical reaction.

_____

3. **Determine** which is the polar end and which is the nonpolar end of the soap molecule.

_____

_____

_____

_____

CHEMLAB 23

Observe Temperature and Enzyme Action

Enzymes are natural catalysts used by living things to speed reactions. These proteins have specialized structures that enable them to interact with specific substances.

Problem

How does temperature affect the action of enzymes?

Objectives

- **Observe** reactions catalyzed by enzymes
- **Compare** the reactivity of enzymes at various temperatures
- **Collect and analyze** data
- **Draw conclusions** based on your analysis

Materials

red-skin potato pulp
hydrogen peroxide(3% H_2O_2)
water
250-mL beaker (4)
test tubes (4)
test-tube rack
test-tube clamp

25-mL graduated cylinder
thermometer
ruler
clock
hot plate
ice
raw fresh liver pulp

Safety Precautions

Pre-Lab

1. Read the entire **CHEMLAB.**

2. Prepare all written materials that you will take into the laboratory. Be sure to include safety precautions and procedure notes.

3. Reread the section of this chapter that describes enzymes. Review the section of **Chapter 16** that describes factors affecting reaction rate.

4. Explain the function of a catalyst.

_____

_____

_____

5. Form a hypothesis about the effect of temperature on enzyme behavior. Use the terms *denature, energy,* and *induced fit* in your explanation.

_____

_____

_____

Procedure

1. Read and complete the lab safety form.

2. Write a hypothesis that identifies the temperature at which the enzyme is the most active.

3. Copy the data table below on a separate sheet of paper to record your data.

Data Table		
Water Bath	**Temperature (°C)**	**Height of Foam (cm)**
Potato		
Ice water		
Room-temperature water		
Body-temperature water		
Boiling water (near 100°C)		
Liver		
Ice water		
Room-temperature water		
Body-temperature water		
Boiling water (near 100°C)		

CHEMLAB 23

4. Place the four test tubes in the test-tube rack.

5. Measure and place 2.0 mL of red-skin potato pulp into each test tube.

6. Using the hot plate and ice, prepare water baths in the beakers at four different temperatures: ice water, room-temperature water, body-temperature water, and gently boiling water at or near 100°C.

7. Place one test tube in each water bath using the test-tube clamp.

8. Measure and record the temperature of each water bath.

9. After 5 min in the water baths, measure and place 5.0 mL of 3% H_2O_2 in each test tube.

10. Allow the reaction to proceed for 5 min.

11. Measure the height of the foam produced in each test tube.

12. Dispose of the contents of the test tubes as directed by your teacher, and wash the test tubes.

13. Repeat Steps 4-12 using 2.0 mL of beef liver pulp instead of potato pulp.

14. **Cleanup and Disposal** Dispose of the remaining solutions as directed by your teacher. Wash and return all lab equipment to its designated location.

Analyze and Conclude

1. **Make and Use Graphs** Make a bar graph with temperature on the x-axis and height of foam on the y-axis.

2. **Summarize** How does temperature affect the action of enzymes? Infer why the maximum reaction occurred at the temperature in which it did for the potato and liver.

_____

_____

_____

_____

_____

3. **Recognize Cause and Effect** Which water bath produced the least amount of foam for each material? Propose explanations for why this happened.

_____

_____

_____

4. **Compare and Contrast** Did the experimental data support your hypothesis in Step 2? Explain.

_____

_____

_____

CHEMLAB 23

5. Model Write a balanced reaction for the decomposition of hydrogen peroxide for each reaction. How are the reactions similar and infer why?

_____

_____

6. Error Analysis Identify potential sources of errors for this investigation and suggest methods to correct them.

_____

_____

Inquiry Extension

Design an Experiment Would a change in pH affect the results? Design an experiment to find out.

_____

_____

_____

_____

_____

_____

_____

_____

_____

_____

_____

_____

_____

_____

_____

_____

_____

_____

_____

_____

TEACHING TRANSPARENCY MASTER 70

Enzymes

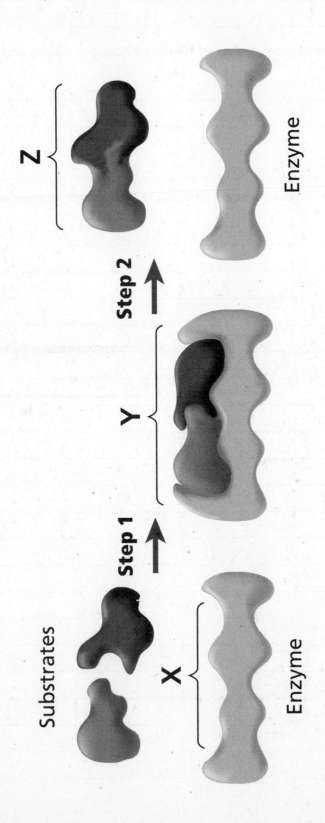

TEACHING TRANSPARENCY WORKSHEET

Enzymes

**Use with Chapter 23,
Section 23.1**

1. What is the area labeled X called?

_____

2. What is Y?

_____

3. What is Z?

_____

4. Explain what is happening at each step in the diagram.

Step 1 _____

_____

Step 2 _____

_____

5. Compare the shape of the enzyme at the beginning and at the end of the reaction.

_____

6. What effect do enzymes have on the following?

a. reaction rate _____

b. activation energy _____

7. How does the large size of enzyme molecules affect their ability to catalyze reactions?

_____

_____

_____

_____

8. What reaction does the enzyme papain catalyze?

_____

_____

9. Name and describe three functions of proteins in addition to their role as enzymes.

_____

_____

_____

_____

TEACHING TRANSPARENCY MASTER

71

Condensation Reactions

Use with Chapter 23, Sections 23.1–23.3

❶

$$H-N-\overset{R_1}{\underset{H}{C}}-\overset{}{\underset{O}{C}}-OH \ + \ H-N-\overset{R_2}{\underset{H}{C}}-\overset{}{\underset{O}{C}}-OH \ \rightarrow \ H-N-\overset{R_1}{\underset{H}{C}}-\overset{}{\underset{O}{C}}-N-\overset{R_2}{\underset{H}{C}}-\overset{}{\underset{O}{C}}-OH \ + \ H_2O$$

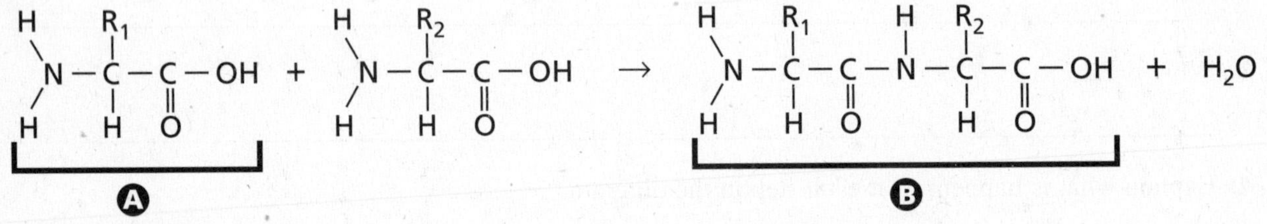

A **B**

❷

$$CH_2OH \quad + \quad CH_2OH \quad \rightarrow \quad CH_2OH \quad CH_2OH \quad + \quad H_2O$$

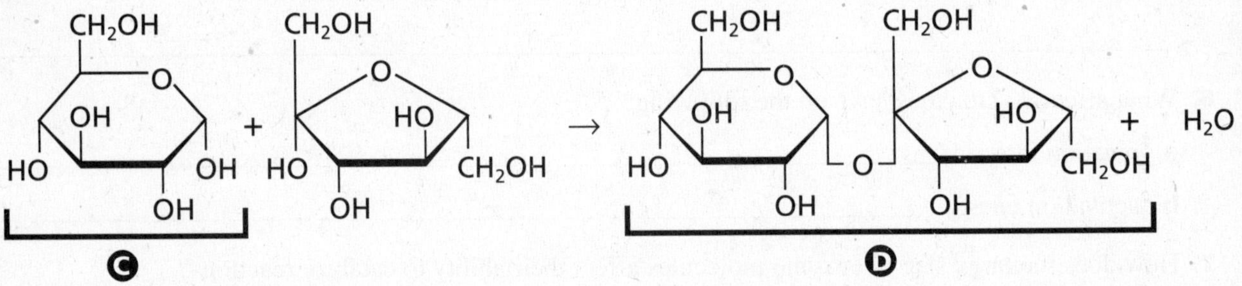

C **D**

❸

$$
\begin{array}{c}
CH_2OH \\
CHOH \\
CH_2OH
\end{array}
\ + \
\begin{array}{c}
HO-\overset{O}{C}(CH_2)_{14}CH_3 \\
HO-\overset{O}{C}(CH_2)_{16}CH_3 \\
HO-\overset{O}{C}(CH_2)_{18}CH_3
\end{array}
\ \rightarrow \
\begin{array}{c}
CH_2-O-\overset{O}{C}(CH_2)_{14}CH_3 \\
CH-O-\overset{O}{C}(CH_2)_{16}CH_3 \\
CH_2-O-\overset{O}{C}(CH_2)_{18}CH_3
\end{array}
\ + \ 3H_2O
$$

E **F**

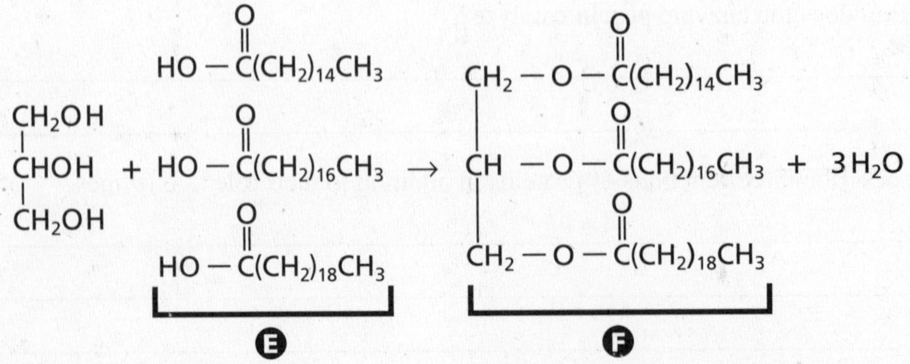

TEACHING TRANSPARENCY WORKSHEET

Condensation Reactions

**Use with Chapter 23,
Sections 23.1–23.3**

1. Identify the type of organic compound represented by each of the letters A–F on the
transparency.

A _____   D _____

B _____   E _____

C _____   F _____

2. What functional group is represented by the bond that is formed in reaction 1?

_____

3. Where does the water that is formed in reaction 1 come from?

_____

_____

_____

4. In reaction 1, is the order in which the two reactants are linked important? Explain.

_____

_____

_____

5. What functional group is represented by the bond that is formed in reaction 2?

_____

6. What is the common name of the three-carbon molecule that reacts with the compounds
labeled E in reaction 3?

_____

7. What functional group is represented by the bonds that are formed in reaction 3?

_____

8. Contrast the water-solubility of reaction products D and F. Explain the difference.

_____

_____

_____

_____

_____

TEACHING TRANSPARENCY MASTER

72

Photosynthesis, Cellular Respiration, and Fermentation

Use with Chapter 23, Section 23.5

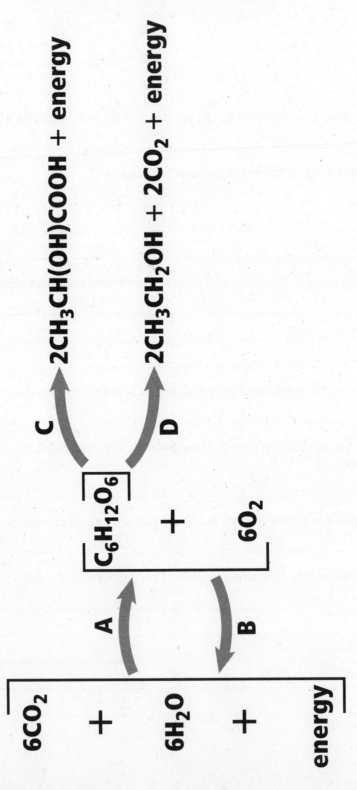

$2CH_3CH(OH)COOH + energy$

$2CH_3CH_2OH + 2CO_2 + energy$

C

D

$C_6H_{12}O_6$ + $6O_2$

A

B

$6CO_2$ + $6H_2O$ + energy

TEACHING TRANSPARENCY WORKSHEET **72**

Photosynthesis, Cellular Respiration, and Fermentation

Use with Chapter 23, Section 23.5

1. Identify the metabolic processes labeled A–D on the transparency.

A _____   C _____

B _____   D _____

2. What kinds of organisms carry out each metabolic process?

A _____

B _____

C _____

D _____

3. Label each metabolic process as anabolism or catabolism.

A _____   C _____

B _____   D _____

4. Identify the following compounds shown on the transparency.

$C_6H_{12}O_6$ _____

$CH_3CH(OH)COOH$ _____

CH_3CH_2OH _____

5. What provides the energy that is used in process A? _____

6. Compare the efficiencies of processes B, C, and D in terms of ATP production.

_____

_____

_____

7. Explain how process C is related to some instances of muscle pain and fatigue.

_____

_____

_____

8. Describe three commercial applications of process D.

_____

_____

Enzyme Activity and pH

**Use with Chapter 23,
Section 23.1**

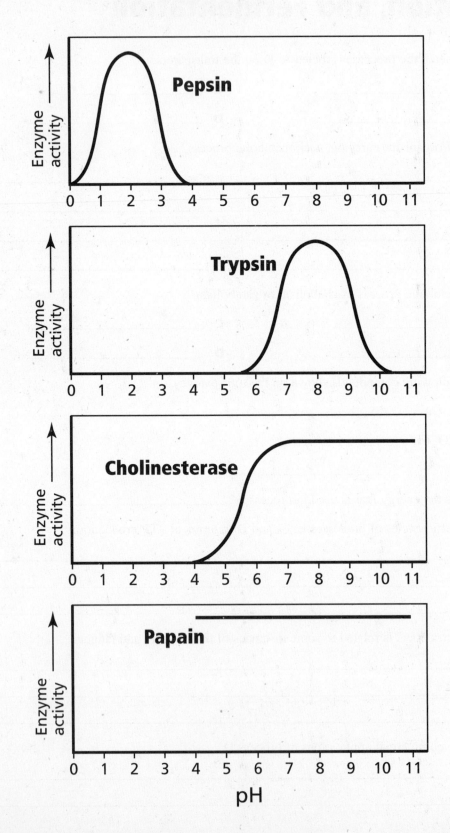

MATH SKILLS TRANSPARENCY WORKSHEET **39**

Enzyme Activity and pH

**Use with Chapter 23,
Section 23.1**

Enzyme activity is a measure of how much an enzyme can speed up a chemical reaction. The four graphs on the transparency show how the activity of four enzymes varies with pH.

1. At what pH is each enzyme most active?

_____

_____

2. Which enzymes would be active to some degree at the following pH values?

pH 3 _____

pH 7 _____

pH 11 _____

3. Which enzyme has an activity that is not affected by pH?

_____

4. Suppose you have a solution of trypsin and a solution of cholinesterase, both at pH 7. You add enough NaOH to change the pH of each solution by one pH unit. How would that pH change affect the activity of each enzyme if the enzyme's substrate was present? Explain your reasoning.

_____

_____

_____

5. Both pepsin and trypsin catalyze the breakdown of proteins as you digest your food. During digestion, your stomach secretes digestive fluid that has a pH of 2, whereas the fluid in your small intestine has a neutral or slightly alkaline pH. In which organ would you expect to find each enzyme? Explain your reasoning.

_____

_____

_____

6. Suppose you have an aqueous solution with an H_3O^+ concentration of $3.2 \times 10^{-5}M$. Which enzymes would be active to some degree in that solution? (Hint: Recall that pH $= -\log [H_3O^+]$.)

_____

MATH SKILLS TRANSPARENCY MASTER

40

From DNA to Protein

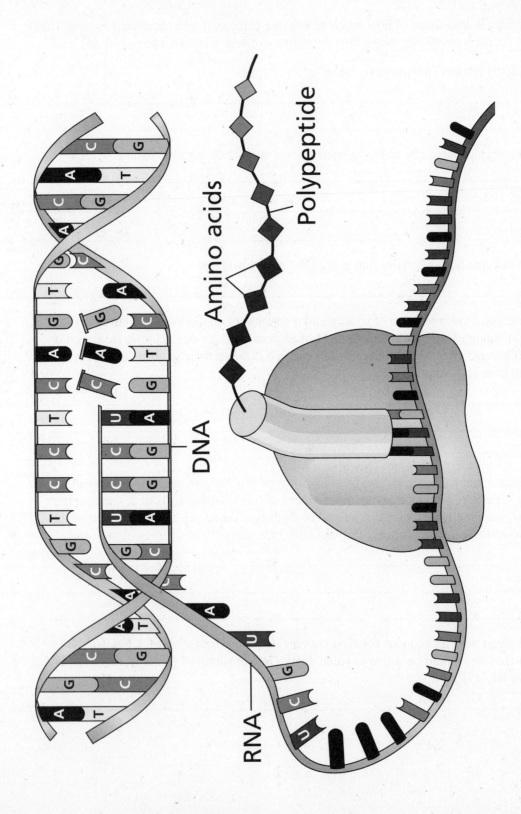

MATH SKILLS TRANSPARENCY WORKSHEET (40)

From DNA to Protein

**Use with Chapter 23,
Section 23.4**

The transparency shows how a bacterial cell uses the genetic information in its DNA to make
a protein with a specific amino acid sequence.

1. The DNA in a bacterial cell contains about 4.2×10^6 nucleotide base pairs. RNA is
    made from DNA at a rate of about 60 nucleotides per second. How long would it take
    a bacterial cell to produce an RNA molecule containing all of the genetic information in
    its DNA?

    _____

    _____

    _____

2. Each amino acid is specified by a group of RNA nucleotides called a codon. The maxi-
    mum number of different amino acids that can be specified is 4^x, where x is the number
    of nucleotides in a codon. How many different amino acids could be specified if $x = 1$?
    If $x = 2$? If $x = 3$? If $x = 4$?

    $x = 1$ _____ $x = 2$ _____ $x = 3$ _____ $x = 4$ _____

3. What is the minimum codon size needed to specify all 20 of the amino acids commonly
    found in proteins?

    _____

4. Suppose a strand of RNA contains 36 nucleotides. If all of the codons in the RNA are
    translated into amino acids, how many amino acids will be in the polypeptide that is
    formed?

    _____

    _____

5. How many different amino acid sequences are possible for a polypeptide that is trans-
    lated from a 36-nucleotide strand of RNA?

    _____

    _____

6. An average-sized protein contains about 400 amino acids. How many RNA nucleotides
    would be needed to code for such a protein?

    _____

    _____

7. How many average-sized proteins could the DNA in a bacterial cell code for?
    (See question 1.)

    _____

    _____

CHAPTER 23 STUDY GUIDE

The Chemistry of Life

Section 23.1 Proteins

In your textbook, read about protein structure.

For each item in Column A, write the letter of the matching item in Column B.

Column A	Column B
_____ **1.** An organic molecule that has an amino functional group and a carboxyl functional group	**a.** denaturation
	b. protein
_____ **2.** A chain of two or more amino acids linked together	**c.** peptide bond
_____ **3.** The process in which a protein's natural three-dimensional structure is disrupted	**d.** amino acid
_____ **4.** An organic polymer made of many amino acids linked together in a specific way	**e.** peptide
_____ **5.** The amide bond that joins two amino acids	

Use the diagram below to answer the following questions.

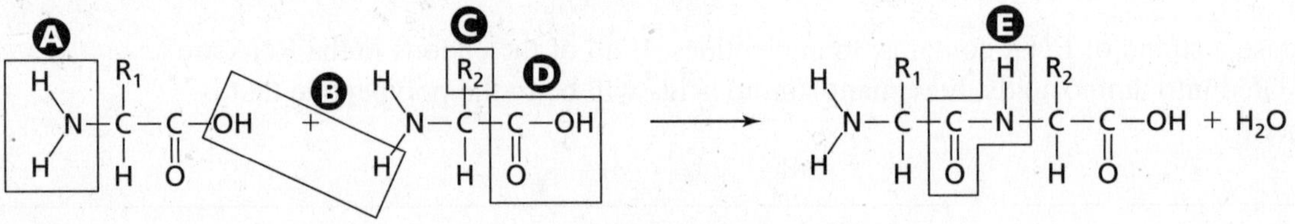

6. Which part (A, B, C, D, or E) is the carboxyl group of an amino acid? _____

7. Which part (A, B, C, D, or E) is the amino group of an amino acid? _____

8. Which part (A, B, C, D, or E) is the side chain of an amino acid? _____

9. Which part (A, B, C, D, or E) is a peptide bond? _____

10. Which part (A, B, C, D, or E) includes the atoms that combine to form water? _____

11. What kind of chemical reaction does this diagram show? _____

12. What kind of organic molecule is formed in this reaction? _____

Section 23.1 *continued*

In your textbook, read about the functions of proteins.

Complete the table below by writing the type of protein described on the left. Choose your answers from the following types: *enzyme, hormone, structural protein, transport protein.*

Functions of Proteins	
Description of function	**Type of protein**
13. Forming a structure that is vital to an organism	
14. Carrying smaller molecules throughout the body	
15. Carrying signals from one part of the body to another	
16. Catalyzing a reaction in an organism	

For each statement below, write *true* or *false*.

_____ **17.** The active site on an enzyme is a specific place where substrates bind.

_____ **18.** Collagen is a protein hormone found in skin, tendons, and bones.

_____ **19.** Most enzymes raise the activation energy of reactions.

_____ **20.** Insulin is an example of a structural protein.

_____ **21.** The reactants in an enzyme-catalyzed reaction are known as substrates.

_____ **22.** Enzymes slow down chemical reactions.

_____ **23.** Hemoglobin is a protein that transports oxygen through the body.

_____ **24.** After the substrates bind to an enzyme, the enzyme's active site changes shape slightly.

_____ **25.** The human body is unable to use proteins as a source of energy.

_____ **26.** Insulin can be synthesized in the laboratory.

Answer the following questions.

27. Why must a molecule have a specific shape if it is to be a substrate of an enzyme?

_____

_____

28. How does being large help an enzyme carry out its function?

_____

_____

Section 23.2 **Carbohydrates**

In your textbook, read about the different kinds of carbohydrates.

Use each of the terms below just once to complete the passage.

polysaccharide	carbohydrate	disaccharide	monosaccharide

A compound that contains multiple hydroxyl groups as well as an aldehyde or ketone

functional group is called a **(1)**_____. A simple sugar, or

(2)_____, is the simplest kind of carbohydrate. Two simple sugars can be

linked together by a condensation reaction to form a **(3)**_____, such as

sucrose. A large carbohydrate polymer made from 12 or more simple sugars is known as

a **(4)**_____.

Circle the letter of the choice that best completes the statement or answers the question.

5. The major function of carbohydrates in living organisms is as a source of
  a. nitrogen.   **b.** hydrogen.   **c.** information.   **d.** energy.

6. How many carbon atoms do most common monosaccharides have?
  a. 1   **b.** 2 or 3   **c.** 5 or 6   **d.** 9 or 10

7. Most simple sugars are water soluble because they have several
  a. polar groups.   **b.** nonpolar groups.   **c.** hydrogen atoms.   **d.** carbon atoms.

8. In aqueous solution, monosaccharides exist as
  a. polymers.   **c.** cyclic structures.
  b. open-chain structures.   **d.** both open-chain and cyclic structures.

9. When two monosaccharides bond to form a disaccharide, the new bond is
  a. a peptide bond.   **b.** an ether bond.   **c.** an alcohol bond.   **d.** a carbonyl group.

10. Glucose and fructose link to form the disaccharide known as
  a. maltose.   **b.** galactose.   **c.** sucrose.   **d.** lactose.

11. Disaccharides are too large to be absorbed into the bloodstream, so they must be broken
  down into
  a. monosaccharides.   **b.** polysaccharides.   **c.** carbon dioxide.   **d.** atoms.

12. Complex carbohydrates are known as
  a. disaccharides.   **b.** polysaccharides.   **c.** monosaccharides.   **d.** simple sugars.

13. Starch, cellulose, and glycogen are all made from monomers of
  a. amylase.   **b.** sucrose.   **c.** lactose.   **d.** glucose.

CHAPTER 23   **STUDY GUIDE**

Section 23.3 Lipids

In your textbook, read about the different kinds of lipids.

Use the following terms to complete the statements.

fatty acid	phospholipid	steroid	wax
lipid	saponification	triglyceride	

1. In a reaction called _____, sodium hydroxide is used to hydrolyze the ester bonds of a triglyceride.

2. Combining a fatty acid with a long-chain alcohol produces a _____.

3. A _____ is a large, nonpolar, biological molecule.

4. A lipid with a four-ring structure is known as a _____.

5. A _____ is a triglyceride in which one of the fatty acids is replaced by a polar phosphate group.

6. A long-chain carboxylic acid is known as a _____.

7. When three fatty acids are bonded to a glycerol backbone through ester bonds, a _____ is formed.

For each statement below, write *true* or *false*.

_____ **8.** All lipids are soluble in water.

_____ **9.** Lipids are an extremely efficient way to store energy in living organisms.

_____ **10.** Most fatty acids have an odd number of carbon atoms.

_____ **11.** Fatty acids that contain no double bonds are called unsaturated.

_____ **12.** Saturated fatty acids have higher melting points than unsaturated fatty acids.

_____ **13.** All lipids contain one or more fatty acid chains.

_____ **14.** A typical cell membrane is a single layer of phospholipids.

_____ **15.** Saponification is a process for making soap out of fats and oils.

_____ **16.** The lipid bilayer of the cell membrane acts as a barrier.

_____ **17.** The wax that coats plant leaves prevents water loss.

_____ **18.** Cholesterol and vitamin D are steroids.

CHAPTER 23   **STUDY GUIDE**

Section 23.4 Nucleic Acids

In your textbook, read about the structure of nucleic acids and of DNA.

Use the diagram of DNA to answer the following questions.

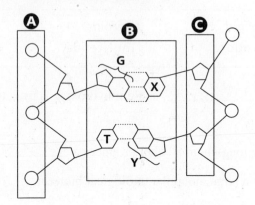

1. Which part (A, B, or C) represents the sugar molecules? _____

2. What is the name of these sugar molecules? _____

3. Which part (A, B, or C) represents the phosphate groups? _____

4. Which part (A, B, or C) represents the nitrogen bases? _____

5. What do the dotted lines represent? _____

6. If the part labeled G is guanine, what must the part labeled X be? _____

7. If the part labeled T is thymine, what must the part labeled Y be? _____

In your textbook, read about the function of DNA and about RNA.

Circle the letter of the choice that best completes the statement.

8. The main function of DNA is to store a cell's
   - **a.** excess fat.
   - **b.** genetic information.
   - **c.** energy reserves.
   - **d.** phosphate groups.

9. The instructions in a DNA molecule are carried in the form of a specific sequence of
   - **a.** hydrogen bonds.   **b.** sugars.   **c.** phosphate groups.   **d.** nitrogen bases.

10. RNA is usually
    - **a.** single stranded.   **b.** double stranded.   **c.** triple stranded.   **d.** a monomer.

11. The order of nitrogen bases in RNA determines the sequence of
    - **a.** simple sugars in a polysaccharide.
    - **b.** fatty acids in a triglyceride.
    - **c.** amino acids in a protein.
    - **d.** phosphate groups in DNA.

Section 23.5 Metabolism

In your textbook, read about anabolism and catabolism.

For each item in Column A, write the letter of the matching item in Column B.

Column A	Column B
_____ **1.** The complete set of reactions carried out by an organism	**a.** catabolism
_____ **2.** A nucleotide that functions as the universal usable energy form in living cells	**b.** metabolism
_____ **3.** Metabolic reactions that synthesize complex molecules needed by an organism	**c.** anabolism
_____ **4.** Metabolic reactions that break down complex biological molecules	**d.** ATP

For each statement below, write *anabolism* or *catabolism*.

_____ **5.** Starch is broken down into glucose monomers.

_____ **6.** Amino acids are linked by peptide bonds to form proteins.

_____ **7.** DNA is synthesized from free nucleotides.

_____ **8.** The proteins in food are broken down into individual amino acids.

_____ **9.** Three fatty acids combine with glycerol to make a triglyceride.

In your textbook, read about photosynthesis, cellular respiration, and fermentation.

For each statement below, write *true* or *false*.

_____ **10.** During photosynthesis, carbohydrates are made from oxygen and glucose.

_____ **11.** Plant cells can carry out photosynthesis, but animal cells cannot.

_____ **12.** The net equation for cellular respiration is the reverse of the net equation for photosynthesis.

_____ **13.** Fermentation is more efficient than cellular respiration at extracting energy from glucose.

_____ **14.** In alcoholic fermentation, glucose is converted to ethanol and carbon dioxide.

_____ **15.** Muscle cells carry out lactic acid fermentation when they have too much oxygen.

The Chemistry of Life

Reviewing Vocabulary

In the space at the left, write _true_ if the statement is true; if the statement is false, change the italicized word or phrase to make it true.

_____ **1.** _Lipids_ are compounds that contain multiple hydroxyl groups as well as an aldehyde or ketone functional group.

_____ **2.** Substrates bind to a pocket known as an _active site_ on an enzyme.

_____ **3.** _ATP_ functions as the universal energy-storage molecule in living cells.

_____ **4.** _Fatty acids_ are organic molecules that have an amino functional group and a carboxyl functional group.

_____ **5.** An enzyme speeds up a chemical reaction by _raising_ the activation energy of the reaction.

_____ **6.** Nucleic acids are involved in the storage and transmission of _genetic information_.

_____ **7.** A _steroid_ is a lipid that is formed by combining a fatty acid with a long-chain alcohol.

_____ **8.** The amide bond that joins two amino acids is known as a _peptide bond_.

_____ **9.** A lipid is a large, _polar_, biological molecule.

_____ **10.** A polymer made of 12 or more simple sugars is called a _protein_.

Compare and contrast each pair of related terms.

11. anabolism, catabolism

_____

_____

_____

_____

12. photosynthesis, cellular respiration

_____

_____

_____

_____

CHAPTER 23

Understanding Main Ideas (Part A)

In the space at the left, write the term in parentheses that correctly completes the statement.

_____ **1.** (Steroids, Waxes) are lipids that have multiple cyclic rings.

_____ **2.** Proteins are organic polymers made of (nucleic acids, amino acids) linked together in a specific way.

_____ **3.** The simplest carbohydrates are known as (monosaccharides, starches).

_____ **4.** The building block of many lipids is the (amino acid, fatty acid).

_____ **5.** A (catalyst, substrate) is a reactant in an enzyme-catalyzed reaction.

_____ **6.** A typical cell membrane has two layers of (phospholipids, polypeptides).

_____ **7.** The thousands of chemical reactions that take place in an organism are known as (metabolism, oxidation).

_____ **8.** A (simple sugar, peptide) is a chain of two or more amino acids linked together.

Use the following terms to complete the statements.

denaturation	fermentation	saponification	disaccharide
nucleotide	triglyceride	uracil	thymine

9. A _____ is formed when two simple sugars are linked together.

10. The monomer that makes up a nucleic acid is called a(n) _____.

11. _____ is used to make soaps out of fats and oils.

12. Cells use _____ to extract energy from glucose in the absence of oxygen.

13. A(n) _____ is formed when three fatty acids are bonded to glycerol.

14. _____ is the process in which a protein's natural three-dimensional structure is disrupted.

15. In a DNA molecule, adenine forms hydrogen bonds with _____.

16. RNA contains the nitrogen base _____.

CHAPTER 23

Understanding Main Ideas (Part B)

Complete the diagram by writing each of the following terms under either "Building Blocks" or "Complex Molecules."

amino acids	fatty acids	nucleic acids	nucleotides
polysaccharides	proteins	monosaccharides	triglycerides

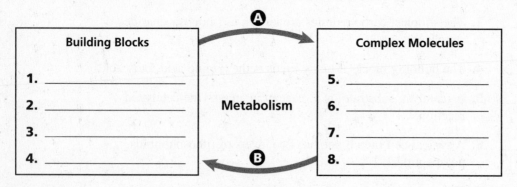

Building Blocks

1. _____

2. _____

3. _____

4. _____

Metabolism

Complex Molecules

5. _____

6. _____

7. _____

8. _____

Use the diagram to answer questions 9 and 10.

9. What set of metabolic reactions is represented by arrow A? _____

10. What set of metabolic reactions is represented by arrow B? _____

Answer the following questions.

11. Why do changes in temperature or pH often affect the shape of proteins?

_____

_____

_____

_____

12. Both starch and cellulose are polymers of glucose, but they have very different properties. Why?

_____

_____

_____

13. How are phospholipid molecules arranged in cellular membranes?

_____

_____

_____

CHAPTER 23

Thinking Critically

Suppose a scientist wishes to analyze the structure of a section of DNA. To separate the two nucleotide chains in the DNA, the scientist carefully heats the DNA to a temperature of 98°C. The sequence of nucleotides in one of the chains is then determined to be the following:

C-A-G-G-T-C-A-T-A

Answer the following questions.

1. The covalent bonds in DNA remain stable at 98°C. Why, then, does heating DNA to this temperature cause the nucleotide chains to separate?

_____

_____

2. What is the sequence of nucleotides in the complementary chain of DNA?

_____

3. What is the sequence of nucleotides in the RNA that would be made from the DNA chain shown above in the box?

_____

4. Suppose one of the nucleotides in a DNA chain were replaced with a different kind of nucleotide. What might happen if such an altered DNA chain were used to make a protein? Explain.

_____

_____

_____

_____

5. Suppose several nucleotides were taken out of a DNA chain. What might happen if such an altered DNA chain were used to make a protein? Explain.

_____

_____

_____

6. Why must a cell keep its DNA sequence intact if the cell is to function normally?

_____

_____

_____

_____

CHAPTER 23   **CHAPTER ASSESSMENT**

Applying Scientific Methods

Two students conducted an experiment to determine whether skim milk contains carbohydrate, protein, or lipid. To look for these substances, the students performed three chemical tests. Each test is specific for one of the substances.

Test #1: To look for carbohydrate, the students added an indicator called Benedict's solution to 1 mL of skim milk in a test tube. They placed the tube in boiling water for 2 minutes and then removed the tube. When the tube had cooled, they looked for a colored precipitate in the tube. They also performed this test on a tube containing 1 mL of distilled water and a tube containing 1 mL of glucose solution.

Test #2: To look for protein, the students added Biuret reagent to 1 mL of skim milk in a test tube. Then they stirred the mixture and looked for a color change. They also performed this test on a tube containing 1 mL of distilled water and a tube containing a 1-mL solution of albumin, a protein.

Test #3: To look for lipid, the students added an indicator called Sudan III solution to 1 mL of skim milk in a test tube. Then they stirred the mixture and looked for a color change. They also performed this test on a tube containing 1 mL of distilled water and a tube containing 1 mL of vegetable oil.

The following table shows the students' results:

Test-Tube Contents	Result
Skim milk + Benedict's solution	No precipitate
Distilled water + Benedict's solution	No precipitate
Glucose solution + Benedict's solution	Orange precipitate
Skim milk + Biuret reagent	Solution changes to purple color
Distilled water + Biuret reagent	No color change
Albumin solution + Biuret reagent	Solution changes to purple color
Skim milk + Sudan III solution	No color change
Distilled water + Sudan III solution	No color change
Vegetable oil + Sudan III solution	Solution changes to pink color

Answer the following questions.

1. Why did the students perform each test on a tube containing distilled water?

_____

_____

2. Why did the students perform test #1 on a tube containing glucose solution?

_____

_____

Applying Scientific Methods, *continued*

3. Why did the students perform test #2 on a tube containing albumin solution?

_____

_____

_____

4. Why did the students perform test #3 on a tube containing vegetable oil?

_____

_____

_____

5. Based on the students' results, which of the three substances (carbohydrate, protein, and lipid) is present in skim milk? Explain how you drew this conclusion.

_____

_____

_____

6. Examine the table for tests with skim milk where there was a negative result: no precipitate or no color change. One explanation for a negative result is that skim milk lacks any trace of the substance that was tested for. What is another possible explanation for a negative result in these tests?

_____

_____

_____

_____

7. Skim milk contains lactose, a disaccharide. Based on what you have read about carbohydrates in Chapter 24, give a possible reason why the skim milk did not form a precipitate in test #1.

_____

_____

_____

8. Lactose can be broken down into glucose and galactose by heating. Suppose the students had performed test #1 after heating the skim milk. What result do you think they would have obtained? Why?

_____

_____

_____

CHAPTER 23
Assessment
Student Recording Sheet

Standardized Test Practice

Multiple Choice

Select the best answer from the choices given, and fill in the corresponding circle.

1. Ⓐ Ⓑ Ⓒ Ⓓ   3. Ⓐ Ⓑ Ⓒ Ⓓ   5. Ⓐ Ⓑ Ⓒ Ⓓ   7. Ⓐ Ⓑ Ⓒ Ⓓ
2. Ⓐ Ⓑ Ⓒ Ⓓ   4. Ⓐ Ⓑ Ⓒ Ⓓ   6. Ⓐ Ⓑ Ⓒ Ⓓ   8. Ⓐ Ⓑ Ⓒ Ⓓ

Short Answer

Answer each question with complete sentences.

9. _____

10. _____

11. _____

12. _____

Extended Response

Answer each question with complete sentences.

13. _____

_____

_____

_____

14. _____

_____

_____

SAT Subject Test: Chemistry

15. Ⓐ Ⓑ Ⓒ Ⓓ Ⓔ   16. Ⓐ Ⓑ Ⓒ Ⓓ Ⓔ   17. Ⓐ Ⓑ Ⓒ Ⓓ Ⓔ

Table of Contents

Chapter 24 Nuclear Chemistry

miniLAB 24

Modeling Radioactive Decay

How do radioactive isotopes decay?

Materials 100 pennies, 5-oz or larger plastic cup, graph paper, shoebox, graphing calculator (optional)

Procedure

1. Read and complete the lab safety form.
2. Place 100 pennies in a plastic cup.
3. Place your hand over the top of the cup and shake the cup several times.
4. Pour the pennies into a shoebox. Remove all the pennies that are "heads-up." These pennies represent atoms of the radioisotope that have undergone radioactive decay.
5. Prepare a data table to record the number of remaining pennies (tail-up pennies).
6. Count the number of pennies that remain and record this number in your data table.
7. Place all of the "tails-up" pennies back in the plastic cup.
8. Repeat Steps 2 through 7 as many times as needed until no pennies remain.

Analysis

1. **Construct** a graph of *Trial number* versus *Number of pennies remaining* from your data table. Draw a curve through the plotted points.

2. **Calculate** how many trials it took for 50%, 75%, and 90% of the sample to decay.

   _____

   _____

   _____

3. **Evaluate** the half-life of the radioisotope if the time between each trial is 1 min.

   _____

4. **Determine** how the results would change if you used 100 dice instead of pennies. In this case, you would assume that any dice that lands with the six side facing up represents a decayed atom and is removed.

   _____

   _____

CHEMLAB 24

Investigate Radiation Dosage

Radiation is a term that causes fearful responses in people. However, not all radiation is dangerous. We are surrounded by radiation from space and from natural radioactivity on Earth. Radiation can also be used in a safe and controlled way for medical purposes.

Problem

What methods are effective in minimizing exposure to radiation?

Objectives

- **Measure** background radiation and radiation emitted by a radioactive isotope
- **Compare** the ability of different materials to shield radiation
- **Collect and analyze** data
- **Draw conclusions** based on your analysis

Materials

alpha source
beta source
gamma source
Geiger counter
piece of cardboard
piece of plastic
meterstick
clock

Safety Precautions

Pre-Lab

1. Read the entire **CHEMLAB.**

2. Prepare all written materials that you will take into the laboratory. Be sure to include safety precautions and procedure notes. Use the data tables below.

Data Table	
Distance	**Geiger Counter Reading (CPM)**
Alpha source	
10 cm	
20 cm	
30 cm	
Beta source	
10 cm	

20 cm	
30 cm	
Gamma source	
10 cm	
20 cm	
30 cm	

Data Table		
Source (positioned at 10 cm)	**Geiger Counter Reading (CPM)**	**Geiger Counter Reading (CPM)**
	Cardboard barrier	**Plastic barrier**
Alpha		
Beta		
Gamma		

CHEMLAB (24)

Data Table	
Source (positioned at 30 cm)	**Geiger Counter Reading (CPM)**
Cardboard barrier at 10 cm	
Alpha	
Beta	
Gamma	
Cardboard barrier at 10 cm	
Alpha	
Beta	
Gamma	

3. What is an isotope? A radioactive isotope?

_____

_____

_____

4. Write the nuclear equation for the radioactive decay of potassium-40 by beta emission. Identify the "parent" and "daughter" nuclides in the decay.

_____

_____

_____

5. Using nuclide-stability rules, form a hypothesis that explains why calcium-40 should be a more stable nuclide than potassium-40.

_____

_____

_____

Procedure

1. Read and complete the lab safety form.

2. Using what you know about types of radiation, write a hypothesis about how the materials listed above will affect the radiation dose.

3. Create a table to record your data.

4. Place the meterstick on the lab station with the Geiger counter at the zero-end.

5. Place the alpha source at the 10-cm mark, and record the highest reading on the Geiger counter.

6. Repeat the measurement with the source at 20 cm and 30 cm.

7. Repeat Steps 5 and 6 with the beta source and gamma source.

8. Place the alpha source on the 10-cm mark, and place a heavy piece of cardboard between the source and the Geiger counter.

9. Measure and record the highest reading.

10. Place the source on the 30-cm mark and place the piece of cardboard on the 10-cm mark first. Measure and record the radiation.

11. Place the piece of cardboard on the 20-cm mark and repeat the measurement.

12. Place the piece of plastic between the source and counter and record the highest reading.

13. Repeat Steps 8–12 with the beta source and the gamma source.

14. Cleanup and Disposal Return all lab equipment and radiation sources to the designated location. Remember to wash your hands with soap and water after completing the lab.

CHEMLAB (24)

Analyze and Conclude

1. Summarize How does distance affect the amount of radiation from a source?

_____

_____

_____

_____

2. Compare and Contrast Does the experimental data support your hypothesis?

_____

_____

3. Explain Based on the data, explain why you were required to wear goggles and a lab apron in this lab.

_____

_____

_____

4. Recognize Cause and Effect Which radiation source was least affected by the cardboard and plastic shields? Explain why this source is different from the other two sources.

_____

_____

_____

_____

_____

5. Infer Did the position of the piece of cardboard influence the results? Explain why or why not.

_____

_____

_____

6. Observe and Infer What can you say about the penetrating power of X rays based on the fact that you have to wear a lead shield at the dentist to protect your body from radiation?

_____

_____

_____

_____

Inquiry Extension

Research Find references that list and quantify the exposure to radiation that we receive in everyday life. Calculate your average annual exposure, and describe methods that could reduce this dosage.

TEACHING TRANSPARENCY MASTER

Production of Transuranium Elements

Use with Chapter 24,
Section 24.3

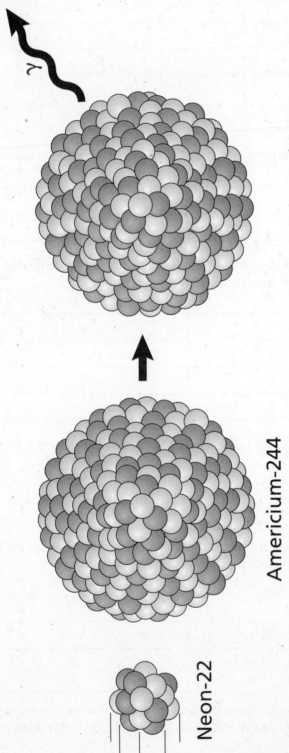

Americium-244

Neon-22

Isotope	Half-Life	Decay Mode
Americium-244	10 hours	Alpha emission
Dubnium-263	30 seconds	Beta emission
Lawrencium-262	3.6 hours	Electron capture
Seaborgium-266	~ 20 seconds	Alpha emission

TEACHING TRANSPARENCY WORKSHEET (73)

Production of Transuranium Elements

Use with Chapter 24, Section 24.3

1. Does the diagram illustrate a natural transmutation reaction or an induced transmutation reaction?

_____

2. What is the name and nuclear symbol of the isotope produced in the reaction?

_____

3. What difficulties do you foresee in trying to carry out the reaction shown here?

_____

_____

_____

_____

4. Write a nuclear equation to show how dubnium-263, lawrencium-262, and seaborgium-266 can be produced from a nuclear reaction of neon-22 and americium-224.

_____

_____

_____

5. Each of the radioisotopes in the table decays within 20 seconds to 10 hours. Write a nuclear equation for each decay.

_____

_____

_____

6. Which, if any, of the four isotopes listed in the table would you expect to find at Earth's surface? Why?

_____

_____

_____

MATH SKILLS TRANSPARENCY MASTER **41**

Balancing Nuclear Equations

❶ $^{238}_{92}U \rightarrow ^{234}_{90}Th + ^{4}_{2}He$

❷ $^{69}_{30}Zn \rightarrow e^- + $ _____

❸ $^{208}_{84}Po \rightarrow ^{4}_{2}He + $ _____

❹ $^{40}_{20}Ca + n \rightarrow ^{41}_{20}Ca + $ _____

❺ $^{233}_{92}U + n \rightarrow ^{92}_{44}Ru + 3n + $ _____

❻ $^{2}_{1}H + ^{2}_{1}H \rightarrow ^{3}_{1}H + $ _____

MATH SKILLS TRANSPARENCY WORKSHEET (41)

Balancing Nuclear Equations

Use with Chapter 24, Section 24.2

1. In equation 1, what do the numbers 238 and 92, written to the left of the symbol U, represent?

_____

_____

2. Explain how both mass number and atomic number have been conserved in equation 1.

_____

_____

_____

_____

_____

3. Write the nuclear symbol for the missing term in equation 2.

_____

4. Write the nuclear symbol for the missing term in equation 3.

_____

5. In equation 4, name the particle represented by the nuclear symbol n.

_____

6. Write the nuclear symbol for the missing term in equation 4.

_____

7. What is represented by the expression 3n in equation 5?

_____

8. Write the nuclear symbol for the missing term in equation 5.

_____

9. Write the nuclear symbol for the missing term in equation 6.

_____

Solving Half-Life Problems

❶ $^{242}_{98}Cf \rightarrow {}^{4}_{2}He +$ _____

$T = 3.5$ min   Original amount: 48.0 g

❷ $^{131}_{53}I \rightarrow e^- +$ _____

$T = 8.0$ days   Original amount: 64.0 g

❸ $^{146}_{64}Gd \rightarrow e^- +$ _____

$T = 48.3$ days   Original amount: 72.0 g

MATH SKILLS TRANSPARENCY WORKSHEET   42

Solving Half-Life Problems

**Use with Chapter 24,
Section 24.2**

1. Write the nuclear symbol for the missing term in equation 1.

_____

2. How much time has passed when 3.0 g $^{242}_{98}$Cf remain?

_____

_____

3. How much $^{242}_{98}$Cf remains after 21 minutes?

_____

4. Write the nuclear symbol for the missing term in equation 2.

_____

5. How long will it take for 60.0 g of the original $^{131}_{53}$I sample to decay?

_____

_____

6. How much $^{131}_{53}$I remains after 56 days?

_____

7. Write the nuclear symbol for the missing term in equation 3.

_____

8. How much of the isotope $^{146}_{64}$Gd remains after 290 days?

_____

9. How much time has passed when 9.00 g $^{146}_{64}$Gd remain?

_____

CHAPTER 24 STUDY GUIDE

Nuclear Chemistry

Section 24.1 Nuclear Radiation

In your textbook, read about the terms used to describe nuclear changes.

Use each of the terms below just once to complete the passage.

alpha particle	radioactivity	gamma ray	radioisotope
beta particles	radiation	X ray	radioactive decay

The discovery of the **(1)**_____ in 1895 by Wilhelm Roentgen opened a

whole new field of research. Among those who worked in this new field were Pierre and

Marie Curie. The Curies discovered that some forms of matter give off

(2)_____, a combination of particles and energy. Marie Curie named this

process **(3)**_____. Another term used to describe the process by which one

element spontaneously changes into another element is **(4)**_____. Any

isotope that undergoes such changes is called a(n) **(5)**_____.

There are three common forms of radiation. One type is a form of energy known as

(6)_____. The other types of radiation consist of particles. The form of

radiation containing the heavier particle is made up of helium nuclei called

(7)_____. The form of radiation containing the lighter particle consists of

electrons called **(8)**_____.

In your textbook, read about the discovery of radioactivity.

Complete each statement.

9. Wilhelm Roentgen discovered the form of energy known as _____.

10. The form of nuclear radiation that has the greatest penetrating power is the _____.

11. When a radioactive nucleus gives off a gamma ray, its atomic number increases by _____.

12. The three types of radiation were first identified by _____.

13. Each alpha particle carries an electric charge of _____.

14. Each beta particle carries an electric charge of _____.

15. Each gamma ray carries an electric charge of _____.

CHAPTER 24   **STUDY GUIDE**

Section 24.2 Radioactive Decay

In your textbook, read about the changes that take place in an atomic nucleus when it decays.

Circle the letter of the choice that best completes the statement.

1. The number of stable isotopes that exist compared to the number of unstable isotopes is

   a. much less.   **b.** much more.   **c.** slightly more.   **d.** about the same.

2. A lightweight isotope is likely to be stable if the ratio of protons to neutrons in its nucleus is

   a. 1:2.   **b.** 1:1.   **c.** 2:1.   **d.** 5:1.

3. The only nucleon among the following is the

   a. electron.   **b.** positron.   **c.** beta particle.   **d.** neutron.

4. The isotope least likely to be found in the band of stability among the following is

   a. $^{13}_{6}$C.   **b.** $^{17}_{8}$O.   **c.** $^{32}_{13}$Al.   **d.** $^{29}_{14}$Si.

5. The isotope formed by the beta decay of $^{40}_{19}$K has an atomic number of

   a. 18.   **b.** 39.   **c.** 20.   **d.** 21.

6. The isotope formed by the alpha decay of $^{238}_{92}$U has a mass number of

   a. 234.   **b.** 236.   **c.** 238.   **d.** 240.

7. The positron produced during positron emission comes from a(n)

   a. neutron.   **b.** proton.   **c.** electron.   **d.** positron.

8. During electron capture, a proton in the nucleus of an atom is converted into a(n)

   a. neutron.   **b.** positron.   **c.** electron.   **d.** another proton.

9. When the isotope $^{238}_{91}$Pa decays by beta emission, the isotope formed is

   a. $^{234}_{89}$Ac.   **b.** $^{238}_{90}$Th.   **c.** $^{237}_{92}$U.   **d.** $^{238}_{92}$U.

10. The isotope formed by the alpha decay of $^{154}_{66}$Dy is

   a. $^{150}_{66}$Dy.   **b.** $^{150}_{67}$Ho.   **c.** $^{150}_{64}$Gd.   **d.** $^{154}_{67}$Ho.

11. The neutron-to-proton ratio for the isotope sodium-23 is

   a. 1 : 1.1.   **b.** 1.1 : 1.   **c.** 2.1 : 1.   **d.** 1 : 2.1.

12. The decay of $^{162}_{69}$Tm yields $^{162}_{68}$Er and

   a. $^{4}_{2}$He.   **b.** e–.   **c.** γ.   **d.** e+ .

13. Atoms located above the band of stability on a graph of numbers of neutrons versus number of protons are usually unstable because they contain too many

   a. protons.   **b.** neutrons.   **c.** electrons.   **d.** nucleons.

CHAPTER 24   **STUDY GUIDE**

Section 24.3 **Nuclear Reactions**

In your textbook, read about the process of induced nuclear transmutation.

For each statement below, write *true* **or** *false*.

_____ **1.** Transmutation is the conversion of an atom of one element to an atom of another element.

_____ **2.** All nuclear reactions involve some type of nuclear transmutation.

_____ **3.** Scientists induce transmutations by bombarding stable nuclei with high-energy alpha, beta, or gamma radiation.

_____ **4.** The first induced nuclear transmutation was carried out by Marie and Pierre Curie in 1897.

_____ **5.** Most induced transmutation reactions are produced in high-energy particle accelerators.

_____ **6.** Neptunium and plutonium were the first transuranium elements discovered.

_____ **7.** The nuclear formula for a neutron is *n*.

_____ **8.** The half-life of a radioisotope is the time it takes for that isotope to decay.

_____ **9.** A radioisotope that decays very rapidly has a short half-life.

_____ **10.** Radioisotopes with very long half-lives are seldom found in Earth's crust.

_____ **11.** Temperature is the only factor that affects the half-life of a radioisotope.

_____ **12.** Carbon dating is not used to measure the age of rocks because the half-life of carbon-14 is too short.

_____ **13.** After an organism dies, its ratio of carbon-14 to carbon-12 and carbon-13 increases.

_____ **14.** Scientists currently believe that all of the possible transuranium elements have been discovered.

_____ **15.** When an atom of $^{125}_{52}$Te is bombarded with protons, the products are $^{125}_{53}$I and neutrons.

_____ **16.** Mass number and atomic number are conserved in all nuclear reactions.

_____ **17.** The mass of a 25.0 g piece of $^{238}_{96}$Cm (half-life: 2.4 hr) will be reduced to 3.1 g after 7.2 hr.

Section 24.3 *continued*

In your textbook, read about the process of by which electrical energy is produced in a nuclear power plant.

Use the following diagram to complete the passage.

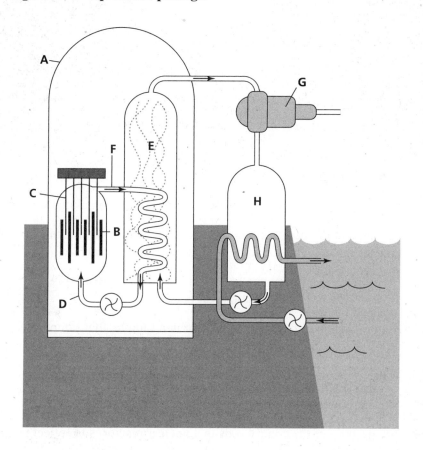

In a nuclear power plant, energy is produced in the reactor core by fission reactions

that occur in uranium-containing bars called **(18)** _____. The uranium is

found at location **(19)** _____ in the diagram. The rate at which the nuclear

reaction takes place is controlled by other bars called **(20)** _____. These bars

of metal are found at location **(21)** _____. One of the important safety factors

in the power plant is a strong dome-shaped structure surrounding the reactor. The structure is

labeled **(22)** _____ in this diagram and called **(23)** _____.

Section 24.3 *continued*

Heat produced by nuclear fission is carried away by **(24)**_____, which enters the core at point **(25)**_____ in the diagram. It then leaves the core at point **(26)**_____.

Heat from the reactor core is used to boil water in the **(27)**_____, shown at **(28)**_____ in the diagram. Steam produced here is used to generate electricity at point **(29)**_____ in the diagram. The steam is then cooled at location **(30)**_____ by water from an outside source.

For each statement, write *true* or *false*.

_____ **31.** A nuclear reactor produces energy from fuel rods containing uranium-238.

_____ **32.** The amount of energy produced for each kilogram of uranium is about the same as the amount of energy from a kilogram of coal.

_____ **33.** The only elements that can be used as fuel in a nuclear power plant are those in which a chain reaction can occur.

_____ **34.** If more than a critical mass is present in a sample, that sample is said to have supercritical mass.

_____ **35.** Water is the most common coolant used in a nuclear reactor.

_____ **36.** Nuclear power plants usually produce electricity.

_____ **37.** The purpose of the control rods in a nuclear reactor is to reflect neutrons back into the core.

_____ **38.** The production of energy in a nuclear reactor can be stopped by pulling out all control rods.

_____ **39.** A breeder reactor produces more fuel than it uses.

_____ **40.** The fission products produced in nuclear power plants are not radioactive.

_____ **41.** An uncontrolled chain reaction led to the nuclear accident in Chernobyl, Ukraine.

Section 24.4 **Applications and Effects of Nuclear Reactions**

In your textbook, read about the methods used to detect and measure radiation.

For each item in Column A, write the letter of the matching item in Column B.

Column A	Column B
	a. PET
_____ **1.** Worn by workers to monitor radiation exposure	
_____ **2.** Contains phosphors that detect radiation	**b.** Geiger counter
_____ **3.** Radiation energetic enough to break apart atoms	**c.** 100–300 mrem
_____ **4.** Uses a gas-filled metal tube to detect and measure radiation	**d.** ionizing radiation
	e. rad
_____ **5.** A material that gives off light when struck by radiation	**f.** iodine-131
	g. rem
_____ **6.** A method used to detect very small amounts of an element in a sample	**h.** genetic damage
_____ **7.** A radioisotope used to indicate the presence of an element in a sample	**i.** neutron activation analysis
	j. scintillation counter
_____ **8.** Used to detect disorders of the thyroid gland	**k.** radiotracer
_____ **9.** A procedure that uses positrons to detect many different medical disorders	**l.** gamma ray
_____ **10.** This type of radiation easily penetrates human tissue.	**m.** somatic damage
_____ **11.** Damage caused by radiation that affects a person, but not their offspring	**n.** phosphor
_____ **12.** Radiation damage that can affect chromosomes and offspring	**o.** TLD badge
_____ **13.** A unit used to measure the amount of radiation absorbed by a body	
_____ **14.** A unit used to measure the amount of damage done to a body	
_____ **15.** The annual amount of radiation to which a person is normally exposed	

CHAPTER 24 CHAPTER ASSESSMENT

Nuclear Chemistry

Reviewing Vocabulary

Match the definition in Column A with the term in Column B.

Column A	Column B
_____ 1. The difference between the mass of a nucleus and the sum of its nucleons	**a.** strong nuclear force
_____ 2. The process in which an atom of one element changes into an atom of another element	**b.** band of stability
_____ 3. A force that acts only on subatomic particles that are extremely close together	**c.** nucleon
_____ 4. A fusion reaction that takes place only at very high temperatures	**d.** radioactive decay series
_____ 5. Isotopes of atoms with unstable nuclei that emit radiation	**e.** induced transmutation
_____ 6. The area on a graph plotting neutrons and protons within which all stable nuclei are found	**f.** thermonuclear reaction
_____ 7. Radiation energetic enough to ionize matter with which it collides	**g.** critical mass
_____ 8. The artificial production of a nuclear reaction that involves striking the nuclei with high-velocity charged particles	**h.** electron capture
_____ 9. A way of determining the age of very old objects using radioactive materials	**i.** mass defect
_____ 10. A form of high-energy electromagnetic radiation	**j.** breeder reactor
_____ 11. A term to describe a sample of fissionable material that is massive enough to sustain a chain reaction	**k.** transuranium element
_____ 12. Another name for a proton or neutron	**l.** ionizing radiation
_____ 13. A radioisotope that emits non-ionizing radiation and is used to signal the presence of an element or specific substance	**m.** transmutation
_____ 14. A series of nuclear reactions beginning with an unstable nucleus and resulting in the formation of a stable nucleus	**n.** radiochemical dating
_____ 15. Any element with an atomic number greater than 92	**o.** radiotracer
_____ 16. A transmutation process brought about when an electron is absorbed by a nucleus	**p.** radioisotope
_____ 17. Reactors able to produce more fuel than they use	**q.** X rays

Understanding Main Ideas (Part A)

Circle the letter of the choice that best completes the statement or answers the question.

1. The person who named radioactivity as the process in which materials give off rays and particles is

  a. Marie Curie.   **b.** Henri Becquerel.   **c.** Wilhelm Roentgen.   **d.** Ernest Rutherford.

2. The most penetrating form of nuclear radiation is

  a. alpha rays.   **b.** beta rays.   **c.** gamma rays.   **d.** positrons.

3. In an atom, the strong nuclear force acts on

  a. protons only.   **c.** protons and neutrons.

  b. neutrons only.   **d.** protons, neutrons, and electrons.

4. During the process of electron capture, an electron from outside the nucleus joins with a proton to form

  a. a neutron.   **b.** a positron.   **c.** another proton.   **d.** a gamma ray.

5. The half-life of calcium-47 is about 5 days. Starting with 64 g of this isotope, what would be the amount remaining after 20 days?

  a. 32 g   **b.** 16 g   **c.** 8 g   **d.** 4 g

6. One product of all nuclear fission reactions is

  a. protons.   **b.** a larger nucleus.   **c.** electrons.   **d.** neutrons.

7. Mass is lost or gained in

  a. all chemical reactions.   **c.** all nuclear fusion reactions.

  b. all nuclear fission reactions.   **d.** all chemical and nuclear reactions.

8. A chain reaction will NOT take place in a piece of uranium if

  a. the temperature is too low.   **c.** there are too few neutrons.

  b. there are too many neutrons.   **d.** the piece of uranium is too large.

9. One of the most serious problems surrounding the use of nuclear power plants is

  a. finding a way to dispose of spent fuel rods.   **c.** a lack of uranium.

  b. the high cost of coolant needed.   **d.** initiating a chain reaction in the fuel.

10. Fusion reactions require

  a. very heavy nuclei.   **c.** very rare elements for use as fuel.

  b. incredibly high temperatures.   **d.** no initial energy.

Understanding Main Ideas (Part B)

Answer the following questions.

1. Listed below are six radioisotopes and the isotopes into which they decay. Tell what kind of radioactive decay takes place in each case.

a. $^{65}_{28}Ni$; $^{65}_{29}Cu$ _____

b. $^{199}_{82}Pb$; $^{199}_{81}Th$ _____

c. $^{190}_{78}Pt$; $^{186}_{76}Os$ _____

d. $^{3}_{1}H$; $^{3}_{2}He$ _____

e. $^{115}_{51}Sb$; $^{115}_{50}Sn$ _____

f. $^{58}_{27}Co$; $^{58}_{27}Co$ _____

2. The five equations below represent nuclear fission and nuclear fusion reactions. For each equation, tell whether fission or fusion has occurred and write the missing term in the equation.

a. $^{3}_{1}H + ^{2}_{1}H \rightarrow ^{4}_{2}He +$ _____

_____

b. $^{235}_{92}U + n \rightarrow ^{95}_{38}Sr +$ _____ $+ 2n$

_____

c. $^{2}_{1}H +$ _____ $\rightarrow ^{3}_{2}He + n$

_____

d. $^{239}_{94}Pu + n \rightarrow ^{88}_{37}Rb +$ _____ $+ 3n$

_____

e. _____ $+ n \rightarrow ^{92}_{39}Y + ^{140}_{53}I + 2n$

_____

3. Manganese-55 is bombarded with alpha particles. The nuclear equation for one possible transmutation reaction is shown below. Complete the other four possible transmutation reactions, given one of the reaction products.

$$^{55}_{25}Mn + ^{4}_{2}He \rightarrow \beta + ^{59}_{28}Ni$$

a. $^{55}_{25}Mn + ^{4}_{2}He \rightarrow n +$ _____

b. $^{55}_{25}Mn + ^{4}_{2}He \rightarrow$ _____ $+ ^{58}_{26}Fe$

c. $^{55}_{25}Mn + ^{4}_{2}He \rightarrow \beta +$ _____

d. $^{55}_{25}Mn + ^{4}_{2}He \rightarrow$ _____ $+ ^{59}_{27}Co$

CHAPTER **24**

Thinking Critically

The graph below shows the trends in mass defect per nucleon for isotopes across the periodic table. The vertical axis shows the relative stability of an isotope on a scale from 1 to 10, 10 being the most stable. Answer the questions below about this graph.

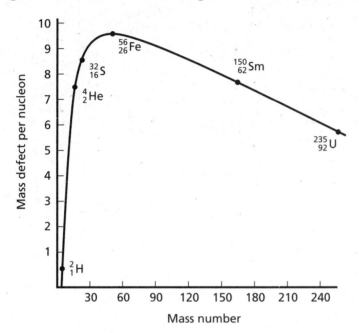

1. What is the least stable of the isotopes shown on the graph? _____

2. What is the most stable of the isotopes shown on the graph? _____

3. What is the relative stability of an isotope of mass number 20?

_____

4. Based on this graph, where are the least stable isotopes likely to be found in the periodic table?

_____

5. Explain why isotopes near the beginning of the periodic table become more stable when they undergo nuclear fusion.

_____

_____

6. Explain why isotopes near the end of the periodic table become more stable when they undergo nuclear fission.

_____

_____

CHAPTER 24

Applying Scientific Methods

The table below shows the results of an analysis done on a recently discovered rock. Answer the following questions about the data in the table.

Radioisotope	Decay Scheme	Half-life	Predicted Order of Abundance
Thorium-232	Alpha emission	1.4×10^{10} years	
Radium-228	Beta emission	6.7 years	
Actinium-228	Beta emission	6 hours	
Thorium-228	Alpha emission	1.9 years	
Radium-224	Alpha emission	3.6 days	

1. Write a nuclear equation for the decay process each radioisotope in the table undergoes.

_____

_____

_____

_____

_____

2. In column 4 of the table, indicate the order of abundance of the radioisotopes. Mark the most abundant isotope <u>1</u>, the second most abundant isotope <u>2</u>, and so on.

3. Explain how you made the decision in question 2.

_____

_____

_____

_____

_____

_____

_____

_____

CHAPTER **24**

CHAPTER ASSESSMENT

Applying Scientific Methods, *continued*

A cloud chamber is a detection device in which a condensation track is formed when ionizing radiation passes through a saturated vapor. The diagram is a representation of a view seen in a cloud chamber. In this diagram, various forms of radiation are given off by a radioactive source (X in the diagram). The upper electric plate is positively charged (+) and the lower electric plate is negatively charged (−). In the spaces provided, identify the four types of radiation shown in this diagram and tell how you decided on each answer.

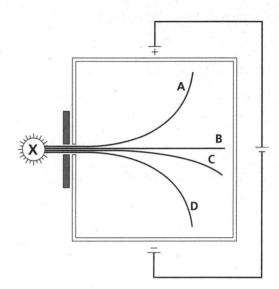

4. Radiation A is _____ because

_____

5. Radiation B is _____ because

_____

6. Radiation C is _____ because

_____

_____

7. Radiation D is _____ because

_____

_____

_____

Describe the track you would expect to see in the above diagram for each of the following types of radiation.

8. A beam of positively charged deuteron (^2_1H) particles:

_____

_____

9. A beam of oxygen ions (O^{2-}):

_____

_____

CHAPTER 24
Assessment | Student Recording Sheet

Standardized Test Practice

Multiple Choice

Select the best answer from the choices given, and fill in the corresponding circle.

1. Ⓐ Ⓑ Ⓒ Ⓓ   3. Ⓐ Ⓑ Ⓒ Ⓓ   5. Ⓐ Ⓑ Ⓒ Ⓓ   7. Ⓐ Ⓑ Ⓒ Ⓓ
2. Ⓐ Ⓑ Ⓒ Ⓓ   4. Ⓐ Ⓑ Ⓒ Ⓓ   6. Ⓐ Ⓑ Ⓒ Ⓓ

Short Answer

Answer each question with complete sentences.

8. _____

9. _____

10. _____

11. _____

Extended Response

Answer each question with complete sentences.

12. _____

_____

_____

_____

13. _____

_____

_____

SAT Subject Test: Chemistry

14. Ⓐ Ⓑ Ⓒ Ⓓ Ⓔ   15. Ⓐ Ⓑ Ⓒ Ⓓ Ⓔ   16. Ⓐ Ⓑ Ⓒ Ⓓ Ⓔ

CHAPTER 21

MiniLab 21 – Synthesize and Observe Ethyne

Analysis

1. Density is slightly less than air.

2. From the color change, students should realize that a base is produced. Given that the cation present is Ca^{2+}, they may infer that the insoluble material is $Ca(OH)_2$.

   $$CaC_2(s) + 2H_2O(l) \rightarrow C_2H_2(g) + Ca(OH)_2(s)$$

Expected Results:

When ignited, the ethyne should pop and burn in a yellow-orange ball that rises from the beaker. Soot may be deposited on the sides of the beaker as a result of incomplete combustion. Ethyne, having a molar mass of 26 g/mol, is slightly less dense than air, which has an average molar mass of about 29. Bubbles may float upward slowly but should demonstrate nearly neutral buoyancy. The phenolphthalein should turn pink as $Ca(OH)_2$ is formed.

ChemLab 21 – Forensics: Analyze Hydrocarbon Burner Gases

Pre-Lab

3. methane (CH_4), 16.04 g/mol; ethane (C_2H_6), 30.07; propane (C_3H_8), 44.10

4. $PV = nRT$; $n = V/RT$

5. a. The experimental molar mass will be larger.

   b. The experimental molar mass will be smaller.

Mass and Volume Data	
Mass of bottle + air (g)	30.49 g
Mass of air (g)	0.82 g
Mass of "empty" bottle (g)	29.67 g
Mass of bottle + collected burner gas (g)	30.30 g
Mass of collected burner gas (g)	0.63 g
Barometric pressure (atm)	1.01 atm
Temperature (°C)	24°C
Temperature (K)	297 K
Volume of gas collected (L)	0.630 L

Analyze and Conclude

1. *mass of air = density × volume*
   See sample data table.

2. See sample data table. At 25°C, approximately 3% of the volume of the bottle will be occupied by water vapor because the gas was collected over water. However, the presence of water vapor may be ignored in an experiment of this precision. Students substitute values into the ideal gas equation and solve for *n*. Students should carry out the following calculation.
   molar mass = measured mass of gas/calculated number of moles

3. Results will depend on the composition of the gas.

4. Possibilities include excess water trapped in the bottle, incorrect or poor measurement techniques, or math error. A gas mixture would yield a molar mass that does not exactly equal the molar mass of any of the components.

Inquiry Extension

Students should find that atmospheric pressure and temperature vary so little in the lab from day to day that they will not affect the results of this type of lab. The measurements are not precise enough to show a difference. However, students that simulate extreme temperature or atmospheric pressure changes might show a difference in their results.

Teaching Transparency 63 – Isomers

1. B, C, and E

2. A and D

3. A

4. D

5. A, B, C, and E

6. A, B, C, D, and E

7. D

8. 2,2-dimethylbutane (on the left) and hexane (on the right)

9. the isomer on the right

10. D

Teaching Transparency 64 – Structure of Benzene

1. six carbon atoms and six hydrogen atoms

2. no

3. It represents three pairs of electrons that are delocalized, or shared among all six carbon atoms in the ring.

4. Answers may vary. Both structures have six carbon atoms and six hydrogen atoms. Both are ring structures.

5. In the structure proposed by Kekulé, the two electrons that form the second bond of each double bond are localized between two specific carbon atoms. In the structure shown on the transparency, these electrons are delocalized.

6. The structure proposed by Kekulé should be more reactive than benzene. Electrons shared by just two carbon nuclei are easier to pull away than electrons shared by six carbon nuclei.

7.

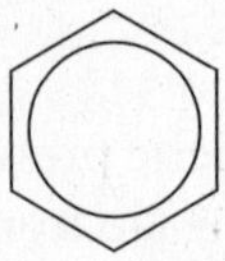

Math Skills Transparency 34 – Naming and Drawing Alkanes

1. butane

2. hexane

3. decane

4. 3-methylhexane

5. 2-methylhexane

6. 3-methylheptane

7. 3, 5-dimethylheptane

8. 4-ethyl 4-polyheptane

9. 3,5-diethyloctane

10. 3, 4, 6, 7-tetraethylnonane

11. 3, 6-diethyl-4-methyl-7-propyldecane

12. cyclopentane

13. 1,2-dimethylcyclobutane

14. 1-ethyl-3-methylcyclohexane

15.
$$CH_3CH_2CHCH_2CHCH_2CH_2CH_3$$
with $CH_2CH_2CH_3$ on the first branch carbon and CH_3 on the second branch carbon

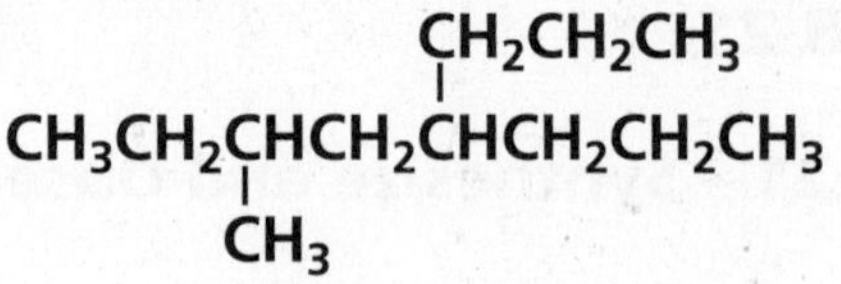

16.
$$CH_3CH_2CCH_2CHCH_2CH_3$$
with CH_3 above, and CH_3 CH_3 below

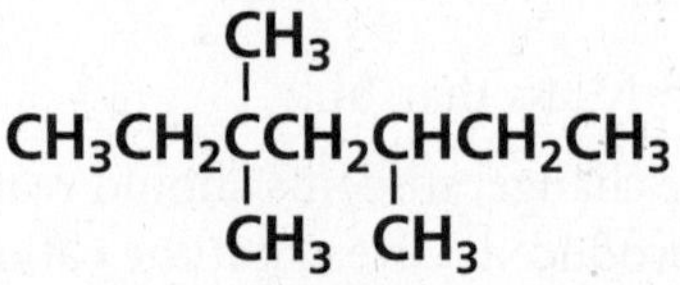

17.
$$CH_3CH_2CHCHCH_2CHCH_2CH_2CH_3$$
with CH_3 above, and CH_2CH_3 $CH_2CH_2CH_3$ below

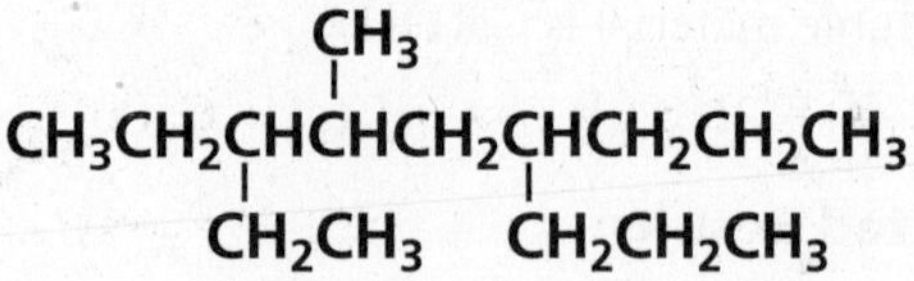

18.
CH_2CH_3, cyclopentane ring with $CH_2CH_2CH_2CH_3$ and CH_2CH_3 branches

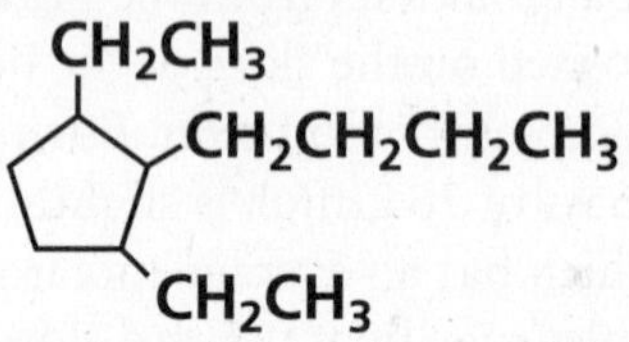

Math Skills Transparency 35 – Comparing Alkanes, Alkenes, and Alkynes

1. a. 2 carbons, 6 hydrogens
   b. 3 carbons, 8 hydrogens
   c. 4 carbons, 10 hydrogens

2. $2n + 2$

3. a. 2 carbons, 4 hydrogens
   b. 3 carbons, 6 hydrogens
   c. 4 carbons, 8 hydrogens

4. $2n$

5. a. 2 carbons, 2 hydrogens
   b. 3 carbons, 4 hydrogens
   c. 4 carbons, 6 hydrogens

6. $2n - 2$

7. The atoms in ethane do not lie in a single plane. The atoms in ethene lie in a single plane. The atoms in ethyne lie along a single line.

Math Skills Transparency 36 – Hydrocarbon Density

1. As the number of carbon atoms increases, the density increases.

2. Alkynes are denser than alkenes, and alkenes are denser that alkanes.

3. grid, cannot input data

4. measured value is 0.749 g/mL; accept values that are close
measured value is 0.758 g/mL; accept values that are close
measured value is 0.779 g/mL; accept values that are close

5. No, slight errors in extrapolating are magnified as you get farther from the plotted data points.

Study Guide - Chapter 21 – Hydrocarbons

Section 21.1 Introduction to Hydrocarbons

1. petroleum

2. fractional distillation

3. cracking

4. octane

5. The temperature is very high at the bottom and gradually decreases toward the top.

6. gas

7. as fuel and to make plastics

8. to make tar, asphalt, and paraffin

9. B

10. A

Section 21.2 Alkanes

1. straight-chain alkanes

2. homologous series

3. true

4. true

5. false

6. octane

7. 2,6-dimethyloctane

8. 
$$CH_3CHCH_2CH_2CH_2CH_2CH_3$$
with CH_3 branch

9. 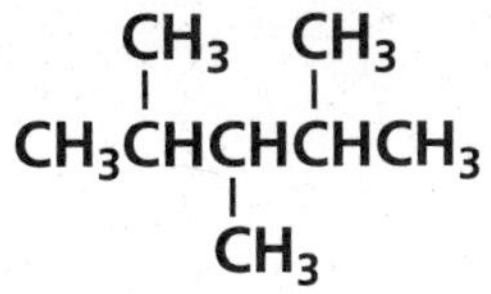
$$CH_3CHCHCHCH_3$$
with CH_3, CH_3 branches above and CH_3 branch below

10. c

11. b

12. a

13. d

14. 1-ethyl-4-methylcyclohexane

15. 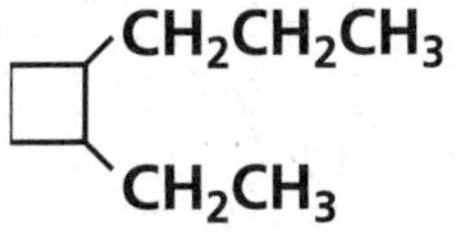
cyclobutane with $CH_2CH_2CH_3$ and CH_2CH_3 substituents

16. nonpolar

17. stronger

18. not very

19. increase

20. low

21. fuels

22. saturated

Section 21.3 Alkenes and Alkynes

1. alkyne

2. ethene

3. alkene

4. ethyne

5. electron density

6. a

7. b

8. 4,4-dimethyl-2-pentene

9. 4-butylcyclohexene

10. 3,7-diethyl-4-decyne

11. 6-ethyl-8-methyl-5-propyl-2-nonene

Section 21.4 Isomers

1. isomers

2. stereoisomers

3. structural isomers

4. optical isomers

5. geometric isomers

6. chirality

7. polarized light

8. optical isomers

9. geometric isomers

10. structural isomers

Section 21.5 Aromatic Hydrocarbons

1. carcinogens

2. aliphatic compounds

3. aromatic compounds

4. a

5. d

6. a

7. c

8. b

9. propylbenzene

10. 1-ethyl-3-methylbenzene

Chapter Assessment - Chapter 21 – Hydrocarbons

Reviewing Vocabulary

1. alkyne

2. saturated

3. structural isomers

4. Optical

5. Branded-chain

6. aromatic

7. carbon

8. true

9. condensed, structural

10. true

11. true

12. heavier

13. true

Understanding Main Ideas (Part A)

1. b

2. d

3. c

4. a

5. c

6. b

7. a

8. c

9. 3-methylheptane

10. 4-ethyl-2-octene

11. 1-ethyl-3-propylcyclohexane

12. 1,2-dimethylcyclohexene

13. 1,3,5-triethyl-benzene

Understanding Main Ideas (Part B)

1. Organic compounds contain carbon, and each carbon atom can form four covalent bonds with carbon or other elements. As a result, carbon atoms can form long chains and an unlimited number of complex, branched structures.

2. In hexane, each carbon atom shares a pair of electrons with the carbon atom or atoms it is bonded to. In benzene, electrons are delocalized, or shared by all six carbon atoms in the ring.

3. B. structural

C. same

4. B. same

C. optical

5. B. same

C. geometric

Thinking Critically

1. Fraction 1: methane, propane, pentane
Fraction 2: hexane, heptane
Fraction 3: octane, decane, pentadecane
Fraction 4: hexadecane

2. nonane: Fraction 3
ethane: Fraction 1
icosane ($C_{20}H_{42}$): Fraction 4

3. 2

The structure shown is (*cis,cis*)-2, 4-hexadine. The other two geometric isomers are the (*trans, trans*) and (*cis, trans*) structures.

4. It would be more difficult to distinguish between two optical isomers. Structural isomers differ in many chemical and physical properties. Optical isomers differ only in their rotation of polarized light and in chemical reactions where chirality is important.

Applying Scientific Methods

1. The tests of molecular formula and solubility in water do not show a difference between A and

B. However, the third test shows that A and B have different reactivities, indicating that they are different compounds.

2. A is more likely to be the saturated hydrocarbon because saturated hydrocarbons are less reactive than unsaturated hydrocarbons, and A has a lower reactivity than B.

3.

Possible saturated hydrocarbons:

ethylcyclopropane   1,1-dimethyl-cyclopropane   1,2-dimethyl-cyclopropane   methylcyclobutane   cyclopentane

Possible unsaturated hydrocarbons:

$CH_2=CHCH_2CH_2CH_3$
1-pentene

$CH_3CH=CHCH_2CH_3$
2-pentene

$CH_2=CCH_2CH_3$ (CH₃)
2-methyl-1-butene

$CH_2=CHCHCH_3$ (CH₃)
3-methyl-1-butene

$CH_3C=CHCH_3$ (CH₃)
2-methyl-2-butene

4. Answers may vary. Properties include melting point, boiling point, and density.

5. A. hexane
   B. mythylcyclopentane
   C. cyclohexane

6. Reaction 1: 2 hydrogen atoms lost; no carbon atoms added or lost
   Reaction 2: no hydrogen atoms or carbon atoms added or lost
   Reaction 3: 6 hydrogen atoms lost, no carbon atoms added or lost

7. D: ethylbenzene
   E: 1-ethyl-2-methylbenzene

8. Answers may vary. With increased production, a chemical becomes more abundant and its price drops. Thus, it is advantageous for industries to look for new ways to use the chemical and for new products that can be made from it. Accept all reasonable answers.

CHAPTER 22

MiniLab 22 – Make an Ester

Analysis

1. Student answers will vary but might include chewing gum and mint candy.

2. Student answers may vary. Advantage: synthetic esters are more efficiently and economically produced than natural esters. Disadvantage: odors of synthetic esters may differ slightly from those of natural esters, which may contain other compounds.

Expected Results:

The product will have a wintergreen odor.

ChemLab 22 – Internet: Properties of Alcohols

Pre-Lab

3. CH_3OH, CH_3CH_2OH, and $CH_3CH(OH)CH_3$. All structures contain the hydroxyl group. Parent chains are different, and the hydroxyl group is on the middle carbon in 2-propanol.

4. hydrogen bonding; 2-propanol likely has the greatest intermolecular forces.

Evaporation Data			
Substance	Starting temp (°C)	Temp after 1 minute (°C)	ΔT (°C)
Water	21	19	2
Methanol	22	8	14
Ethanol	22	13	9
2-Propanol	21	16	5

Analyze and Conclude

1. The greater the heat transfer during evaporation, the greater the temperature change.

2. Intermolecular forces increase as the length of the carbon chain increases. The heat of vaporization is a measure of the strength of these forces.

3. The rate of evaporation appears to decrease as the number of carbon atoms increases.

4. The difference might be due to differences in temperature and humidity in the various labs.

5. The tissue pieces might have varied in size. Air movement around the thermometer might have varied. The amount of alcohol used might have varied in each trial.

Inquiry Extension

Student might suggest that the same amount of alcohol should be added to the tissue paper for each trial. Care should be taken to ensure that the tissue papers are the same size for each trial. A small electric fan might be used to standardize the air movement around the thermometer.

Teaching Transparency 65 – Naming Halocarbons

1. a functional group

2. an alkyl halide

3. chloroethane; no

4. 1,1-dichloroethane; more than one dichloroethane compound can exist, depending on the positions of the chlorine atoms, so numbers are needed to distinguish them.

5. 1,1-dichloroethane; the names are the same because the two compounds are the same. The compounds are simply shown reversed relative to each other.

6. 1,2-dichloroethane

7. The halogens are listed alphabetically. Numbers are assigned so as to give the lowest position number to the halogen that comes first in the alphabet.

8. bromochloromethane

9. 1-bromo-2-chloroethane

10. 2-bromo-2-chloro-3-fluoropentane

11. an aryl halide

12. 1,2-diiodobenzene

13. 1,3-dibromo-4-chlorobenzene

Teaching Transparency 66 – Alcohols, Ethers, and Amines

1. hydroxyl group, OH

2. -ol

3. by means of a number followed by a dash placed at the beginning of the name

4. an oxygen atom bonded to two carbon atoms

5. The alkyl groups are listed in alphabetical order, followed by the word ether.

6. a nitrogen atom bonded to a carbon atom

7. compound A: ethylmethyl ether
compound B: 1-propylamine
compound C: 1-propanol
compound D: 1,3-propyldiamine
compound E: 1,3-propanediol

8. compound B

9. compound A

10. compound B

Teaching Transparency 67 – Carbonyl, Carboxyl, and Amide Groups

1. the carbonyl group, which is made up of an oxygen atom and a carbon atom double-bonded to each other

2. a. pentanal

   b. aldehyde

   c. The compound is polar, it can form hydrogen bonds with water, and its boiling point is lower than that of the corresponding alcohol.

3. a. 3-pentanone

   b. ketone

   c. The compound is polar and can form hydrogen bonds with water.

4. a. pentanoic acid

   b. carboxylic acid

   c. carboxyl group, –COOH

   d. The compound is polar, it ionizes in water, and litmus paper in the resulting solution is red.

5. pentanoate ion

6. E is methyl pentanoate. F is pentanamide.

Teaching Transparency 68 – Kinds of Organic Reactions

1. a substitution reaction

2. E, I

3. I

4. an elimination reaction

5. A, D, H

6. H

7. D

8. an addition reaction

9. B, F, G

10. B

11. F

12. a condensation reaction

13. C

Teaching Transparency 69 – Forming Polymers

1. a. a large molecule consisting of many repeating subunits

   b. a single unit molecule from which a polymer is made

   c. a repeating group of atoms formed by the bonding of monomers

2. a. ethene, C_2H_4

   b. the structural unit of the polymer

   c. polyethylene

   d. Addition; all the atoms in the monomers are retained in the polymer.

3. a. 1,2-ethanediol

   b. the structural unit of the polymer

   c. methanol

   d. Condensation; it occurs with the loss of a small by-product (methanol).

4. a. chloroethene

   b. polyvinyl chloride

Math Skills Transparency 37 – Naming Organic Compounds

1. three

   a. two

   b. four

   c. $3 + 2 + 4 = 9$

   d. six

   e. There must be a total of 14 single bonds to the 6 bonded carbon atoms. Nine are already accounted for by the halogen atoms, so the number of atoms must be $14 - 9 = 5$.

2. two

   a. three

   b. $2 + 3 = 5$

   c. Six; a benzene ring always has six carbon atoms.

   d. There must be a total of six single bonds to the six bonded carbon atoms in the ring. Five are already accounted for by the halogen atoms, so the number of hydrogen atoms must be $6 - 5 = 1$.

3. a. 1,2,2-tribromo-4,4-dichloro-3-fluoroheptane

   b. 1,4-dibromo-3-chloro-4,5,5-triiodocyclooctane

   c. 1,3-dichloro-2,4,5-trifluoro-6-yodobenzene

   d. 1-bromo-2-chloro-4,5-difluorobenzene

Math Skills Transparency 38 – Using *n* to Calculate Molecular Masses of Polymers

1. the repeating group of atoms in the polymer formed by the bonding of monomers

2. the number of structural units that make up the chain

3. Find the mass of the structural unit by summing the masses of the atoms that make up the structural unit, then multiply the sum by *n*.

4. $(1.0 \text{ amu/H} \times 3 \text{ H}) + (12.0 \text{ amu/C} \times 2 \text{ C}) + (35.5 \text{ amu Cl} \times 1 \text{ Cl}) = 62.5 \text{ amu}$

5. $700 \times 62.5 \text{ amu} = 43{,}750 \text{ amu} =$ (rounded) $43{,}800 \text{ amu}$

6. $(1.0 \text{ amu/H} \times 8 \text{ H}) + (12.0 \text{ amu/C} \times 8 \text{ C}) = 104.0 \text{ amu}$

7. $1250 \times 104.0 \text{ amu} = 130{,}000 \text{ amu}$

8. $(1.0 \text{ amu/H} \times 4 \text{ H}) + (12.0 \text{ amu/C} \times 2 \text{ C}) = 28.0 \text{ amu}$

9. $900 \times 28.0 \text{ amu} = 25{,}200 \text{ amu}$

10. $(1.0 \text{ amu/H} \times 22 \text{ H}) + (12.0 \text{ amu/C} \times 12 \text{ C}) + (16.0 \text{ amu/O} \times 2 \text{ O}) + (14.0 \text{ amu/N} \times 2 \text{ N}) = 226.0 \text{ amu}$

11. $1750 \times 226.0 \text{ amu} = 395{,}500 \text{ amu}$

Study Guide - Chapter 22 – Substituted Hydrocarbons and Their Reactions

Section 22.1 Alkyl Halides and Aryl Halides

1. c

2. a

3. a

4. c

5. halocarbon

6. alkyl halide

7. benzene

8. aryl halide

9. optical isomer

10. chiral

Section 22.2 Alcohols, Amines, and Ethers

1. a

2. c

3. d

4. d

5. b

6. a

7. c

8. d

9. b

10. b

11. b

12. d

13. true

14. true

15. false

16. false

17. true

18. true

19. false

20. false

21. c

22. f

23. l

24. h

25. b

26. j

27. e

28. k

29. a

30. i

31. g

32. d

Section 22.3 Carbonyl Compounds

1. b

2. d

3. b

4. c

5. d

6. carboxyl

7. carboxylic acids

8. –oic

9. ester

10. amide

11. proteins

Section 22.4 Other Reactions of Organic Compounds

1. d

2. g

3. a

4. f

5. b

6. e

7. c

8. c

9. b

10. a

11. b

12. b

Section 22.5 Polymers

1. polymer

2. polymerization

3. monomer

4. cellulose

5. celluloid

6. catalyst

7. addition

8. condensation

9. water

10. true

11. true

12. false

13. false

14. true

15. false

16.

$$-CH_2-CH\left[CH_2-CH\right]CH_2-CH-$$
$$\quad\quad\; |\quad\quad\quad |\quad\quad\quad\quad |$$
$$\quad\quad CH_3\;\; CH_3\!\!\Big]_n\;\; CH_3$$

$$CH_2\!\!=\!\!CH$$
$$\quad\quad\;|$$
$$\quad\quad CH_3$$

Chapter Assessment - Chapter 22 – Substituted Hydrocarbons and Their Reactions

Reviewing Vocabulary

1. c

2. k

3. d

4. j

5. b

6. p

7. o

8. a

9. r

10. g

11. n

12. q

13. e

14. s

15. h

16. l

17. i

18. m

19. f

Understanding Main Ideas (Part A)

1. b

2. a

3. c

4. d

5. b

6. a

7. true

8. true

9. water

10. true

11. -one

12. -al

13. less

14. true

15. true

16. condensation

17. An aryl halide

Understanding Main Ideas (Part B)

1. a. The functional group is a carbon atom that is double-bonded to an oxygen atom and bonded to a hydrogen atom.

    b. aldehyde

    c. butanal

2. a. The functional group is an oxygen atom single-bonded to two carbon atoms.

    b. ether

    c. mythelpropyl ether

3. a. The functional group is an oxygen atom double-bonded to a carbon atom that is bonded to other carbon atoms.

    b. ketone

    c. butanone

4. a. The functional group is a hydroxyl group bonded to a carbon atom.

    b. alcohol

    c. 2-butanol

Thinking Critically

1. A polymerization reaction is a reaction in which many small molecules combine to form a very large molecule with repeating structural units.

2. A dicarboxylic acid; it contains two –COOH groups.

3. the repeating group of atoms formed by the bonding of the monomers

4. It is set off by brackets.

5. an amide group

6. Condensation; monomers containing more than one functional group have combined, with the loss of a small by-product.

7. water

Applying Scientific Methods

1. The conclusion that Y is the carboxylic acid is reasonable because only that category of compound, among the four tested, is acidic. The student failed to recognize that the basicity of Z strongly suggests that it is the amine. Both alcohols and ketones are neutral in solution, so no further conclusions can be made about W and X.

2. The student's claim is reasonable. All the compounds are at least somewhat soluble. Without quantitative information and access to tables of specific solubility data, it would be difficult to come to any definite conclusion based on the student's solubility data.

3. The conclusions are valid. Of the four possible categories of compounds, only amines have an ammonia-like odor, and only carboxylic acids smell sour.

4. The conclusion is probably invalid. Aldehydes tend to have lower boiling points than alcohols with the same number of carbon atoms, so it is likely that W, which has the lower boiling point, is the aldehyde, and X is the alcohol.

5. The results indicate that W is the aldehyde, X the alcohol, Y the carboxylic acid, and Z the amine.

6. X is propanol, W is propanal, Y is propanoic acid, and Z is propylamine. The number values for the positions of the functional groups in propanol and in propylamine cannot be determined without referring to handbook values for boiling point.

7. The steps involve those often used in investigating a problem scientifically. A question was initially posed, experiments planned and carried out, observations made, data analyzed, and conclusions reached on the basis of the data.

CHAPTER 23

MiniLab 23 – Observe a Saponification Reaction

Analysis

1. ester bonds

2. glycerol

3. The end of the molecule that contains the sodium ion is polar. The other end of the molecule that contains the hydrogen atoms is nonpolar.

Expected Results:

The small bar of soap can be molded into an evaporating dish.

ChemLab 23 – Observe Temperature and Enzyme Action

Pre-Lab

4. A catalyst lowers the activation energy of a reaction.

5. When an enzyme binds to the substrate, it physically surrounds reactants to facilitate their reaction—a property known as *induced fit*. At low temperatures, the enzyme and reactant substrates lack sufficient energy to properly collide and react. At high temperatures, the protein structure of the enzyme is denatured, preventing binding and induced fit. Because of these factors, enzymes are most effective within a specific range of temperatures.

Analyze and Conclude

1. Refer to Solutions Manual for graph.

2. The enzymes function more as temperature increases until the enzymes are denatured and lose function.

3. The hot water bath, because the enzymes were denatured.

4. Answers will vary.

5. potato: $2H_2O_2 (aq) \rightarrow 2H_2O (g) + O_2 (g)$
   liver: $2H_2O_2 (aq) \rightarrow 2H_2O (g) + O_2 (g)$

6. Possible answers: The contents foamed out of the test tube and the height of the foam was an estimate. A possible method to correct this is to use larger test tubes.

Inquiry Extension

Check student designs.

Teaching Transparency 70 – Enzymes

1. the active site

2. the enzyme-substrate complex

3. the product of the reaction

4. Step 1: The substrates bind to the active site of the enzyme. The active site changes shape slightly to fit more tightly around the substrates.

   Step 2: Bonds are broken and new bonds form to produce the product.

5. The shape of the enzyme is the same.

6. a. increase

   b. decrease

7. It allows enzymes to form multiple bonds of different types with substrates, which makes enzymes more effective catalysts.

8. the breakdown of proteins into amino acids

9. Transport proteins: transport smaller molecules throughout the body.
   Structural proteins: form structures vital to organisms. Hormones: carry signals from one part of the body to another.

Teaching Transparency 71 – Condensation Reactions

1. A. amino acid

   B. dipeptide

   C. monosaccharide

   D. disaccharide

   E. fatty acid

   F. triglyceride

2. amide

3. It comes from the OH in the carboxyl group of one amino acid and one of the H atoms in the amino group of the other amino acid.

4. Yes, the order is important. Reversing the order will produce a different dipeptide.

5. ether

6. glycerol

7. ester

8. D is water soluble because it has multiple hydroxyl groups, which are polar. F is insoluble in water because it has three long hydrocarbon chains, which are nonpolar.

Teaching Transparency 72 – Photosynthesis, Cellular Respiration, and Fermentation

1. A. photosynthesis

   B. cellular respiration

   C. lactic acid fermentation

   D. alcoholic fermentation

2. A. plants, algae, and some bacteria

   B. most organisms

   C. animals

   D. yeast and bacteria

3. A. anabolism

   B. catabolism

   C. catabolism

   D. catabolism

4. glucose, lactic acid, ethanol

5. sunlight

6. Process B (cellular respiration) produces a maximum of 38 moles of ATP per mole of glucose. Processes C (lactic acid fermentation) and D (alcoholic fermentation) each produce only two moles of ATP per mole of glucose.

7. During strenuous exercise, muscle cells use lactic acid fermentation to produce energy. If lactic acid is produced more rapidly than it can be removed by the blood, it accumulates in muscles, causing pain and fatigue.

8. Alcoholic fermentation is used to make bread dough rise, to form tofu from soybeans, and to produce ethanol for gasohol and alcoholic beverages.

Math Skills Transparency 39 – Enzyme Activity and pH

1. pepsin, pH 2; trypsin, pH 8; cholinesterase, pH 7 and above; papain, pH 4 and above

2. pepsin; typsin, cholinesterase, papain; cholinesterase, papain

3. papain

4. Because NaOH is a base, the pH would increase from 7 to 8. Trypsin is most active at pH 8, so its activity would increase. Cholinesterase has the same activity above pH 7, so its activity would not change.

5. You would expect to find pepsin in the stomach because it is most active at pH 2. You would expect to find trypsin in the small intestine because it is most active at pH 8, which is slightly alkaline.

6. pH = −log (3.2 × 10^{-5}) = 4.49. Cholinesterase and papain are active at that pH.

Math Skills Transparency 40 – From DNA to Protein

1. The transparency indicates that RNA is made from one of the nucleotides in each base pair, so all of the genetic information is contained in 4.2 × 10^6 nucleotides. 4.2 × 10^6 nucleotides × (1 s/60 nucleotides) = 7 × 10^4 s, or 19 h

2. 4, 16, 64, 256

3. 3 nucleotides

4. 36 nucleotides × (1 codon/3 nucleotides) × (1 amino acid/codon) = 12 amino acids

5. 20^{12} = 4.096 × 10^{15} sequences

6. 400 amino acids × (1 codon/amino acid) × (3 nucleotides/codon) = 1200 nucleotides

7. 4.2 × 10^6 nucleotides × (1 protein/1200 nucleotides) = 3500 proteins

Study Guide - Chapter 23 – The Chemistry of Life

Section 24.1 Proteins

1. d

2. e

3. a

4. b

5. c

6. D

7. A

8. C

9. E

10. B

11. a condensation reaction

12. a dipeptide

13. structural protein

14. transport protein

15. hormone

16. enzyme

17. true

18. false

19. false

20. false

21. true

22. false

23. true

24. true

25. false

26. true

27. The shape of the molecule must fit the shape of the enzyme's active site.

28. Being large allows an enzyme to form multiple bonds with its substrates, which lowers the activation energy of the reaction the enzyme catalyzes.

Section 23.2 Carbohydrates

1. carbohydrate

2. monosaccharide

3. disaccharide

4. polysaccharide

5. d

6. c

7. a

8. d

9. b

10. c

11. a

12. b

13. d

Section 23.3 Lipids

1. saponification

2. wax

3. lipid

4. steroid

5. phospholipid

6. fatty acid

7. triglyceride

8. false

9. true

10. false

11. false

12. true

13. false

14. false

15. true

16. true

17. true

18. true

Section 23.4 Nucleic Acids

1. C

2. deoxyribose

3. A

4. B

5. hydrogen bonds

6. cytosine

7. adenine

8. b

9. d

10. a

11. c

Section 23.5 Metabolism

1. b

2. d

3. c

4. a

5. catabolism

6. anabolism

7. anabolism

8. catabolism

9. anabolism

10. false

11. true

12. true

13. false

14. true

15. false

Chapter Assessment - Chapter 23 – The Chemistry of Life

Reviewing Vocabulary

1. Carbohydrates

2. true

3. true

4. Amino acids

5. lowering

6. true

7. wax

8. true

9. nonpolar

10. polysaccharide

11. Both terms refer to metabolic reactions. Anabolism refers to reactions that use energy and small building blocks to synthesize complex molecules. Catabolism refers to reactions that break down complex molecules into smaller building blocks, releasing energy.

12. Both are metabolic reactions. Photosynthesis uses carbon dioxide, water, and the energy of sunlight to produce glucose and oxygen. During cellular respiration, glucose and oxygen are used to produce carbon dioxide and water, releasing energy.

Understanding Main Ideas (Part A)

1. Steroids

2. amino acids

3. monosaccharides

4. fatty acid

5. substrate

6. phospholipids

7. metabolism

8. peptide

9. disaccharide

10. nucleotide

11. saponification

12. fermentation

13. trigliceride

14. denaturation

15. thymine

16. uracil

Understanding Main Ideas (Part B)

1. amino acids

2. fatty acids

3. nucleotides

4. monosaccharides

5. nucleoc acids

6. polysaccharides

7. protiens

8. triglycerides

9. anabolism

10. catabolism

11. The shape of a protein is determined by hydrogen bonds and van der Waals forces among the amino acids in the protein. Changing the temperature or pH can disrupt these interactions, causing the protein to unfold and uncoil, which changes its normal shape.

12. The spatial orientation of the bonds between the glucose molecules in starch is different from that in cellulose.

13. A cellular membrane has two layers of phospholipids. In each layer, the polar heads of the phospholipids point outward and the nonpolar tails point into the center of the membrane.

Thinking Critically

1. The nucleotide chains are held together by hydrogen bonds, which are disrupted by this increase in temperature.

2. G-T-C-C-A-G-T-A-T

3. G-U (uracil)-C-C-A-G-U-A-U

4. The sequence of nucleotides in DNA determines the sequence of nucleotides in RNA, which determines the sequence of amino acids in a protein. Therefore, the altered DNA might

lead to a protein with a different amino acid in a certain position.

5. The RNA that is made from the altered DNA would also be missing some nucleotides. The protein that is made from this RNA would be missing one or more amino acids.

6. Changes in the DNA sequence would cause the cell to make proteins with altered amino acid sequences. These proteins might not be able to carry out their specific functions. Since proteins control most of the activities in a cell, a cell with altered proteins probably would not function normally.

Applying Scientific Methods

1. The tubes containing distilled water served as controls. They showed what results to expect if a substance contains no carbohydrate, protein, or lipid.

2. Since glucose is a carbohydrate, the tube containing glucose solution showed what result to expect from test #1 if the skim milk contained a carbohydrate.

3. Since albumin is a protein, the tube containing albumin solution showed what result to expect from test #2 if the skim milk contained a protein.

4. Since vegetable oil is a lipid, the tube containing vegetable oil showed what result to expect from test #3 if the skim milk contained a lipid.

5. The results indicate that protein is present in skim milk. Test #2 produced the same color change with skim milk that it produced with the solution of albumin, a known protein.

6. Answers may vary. One possible explanation is that skim milk contains the substances but at levels too low to be detected by the tests. Another possible explanation is that skim milk contains certain types of carbohydrates or lipids that are not detected by the tests.

7. Answers may vary. Although Benedict's solution can detect glucose, a monosaccharide, it may not be able to detect disaccharides.

8. They would have seen an orange precipitate. Heating would have produced glucose and galactose, which would have reacted with the Benedict's solution to form the precipitate.

CHAPTER 24

MiniLab 24 – Modeling Radioactive Decay

Analysis

1. The graph should show an exponential decay, and in general should resemble the shape of the curve seen in Figure 24.11.

2. It took approximately one trial for 50% of the sample to decay. It took approximately two trials for 75% of the sample to decay. It took approximately four trials for 90% of the sample to decay.

3. The half-life is 1 minute.

4. Approximately one-sixth of the dice will decay with each toss. It would take approximately three tosses to get one-half of the sample to decay.

Expected Results:

The Decay Results table should show that approximately half of the pennies decay during each trial. There will probably be no pennies remaining after 7 to 9 trials.

ChemLab 24 – Investigate Radiation Dosage

Pre-Lab

3. Isotopes are atoms of the same element that have the same atomic number but different atomic masses due to having different numbers of neutrons. A radioactive isotope, also known as a radioisotope, is an unstable isotope that will undergo radioactive decay.

4. $^{40}_{19}K \rightarrow {}^{40}_{20}Ca + \beta$

   parent $\rightarrow$ daughter $+ \beta$

5. Potassium-40 has an n/p ratio of 21 : 19, or 1.105 : 1. Calcium-40 has an n/p ratio of 20 : 20, or 1 : 1. Calcium-40's lower n/p ratio makes it more stable.

Radiation Level Data	
Data point	Counts/min
1	21.9
2	17.5
3	17.4
4	19.2
5	19.2
6	43.3
7	76.5
8	79.3
9	93.3
10	67.0
11	65.0
12	54.6

Analyze and Conclude

1. As the distance from a radiation source increases, the values obtained decrease dramatically.

2. Answers will vary. Students might be surprised to find that shielding does not stop gamma-rays.

3. The goggles and apron provide shielding from some of the radiation.

4. The gamma-rays were not affected by the shields. The gamma-rays are pure energy. This is due to the energy of the particles decreasing as they travel from the source.

5. The particle radiation (alpha and beta) was shielded more as the distance from the source to the shield increased. This is due to the energy of the particles decreasing as they travel from the source.

6. X-ray technicians use distance and shielding to reduce their exposure. The lead shield provides you protection from unnecessary exposure to X rays. From this you can infer that X rays cannot penetrate lead or the walls of the room.

Inquiry Extension

Answers will vary. The students should find a source such as the EPA online calculator and calculate their annual radiation dose. The American Nuclear Society is also a good resource of information.

Teaching Transparency 73 – Production of Transuranium Elements

1. induced transmutation

2. dubnium-266; $^{266}_{105}\text{Db}$

3. Large amounts of energy are needed to make the neon nucleus collide with the americium nucleus. Unstable Am-244 must be prepared before the induced transmutation reaction can be performed.

4. $^{22}_{10}\text{Ne} + ^{244}_{95}\text{Am} \longrightarrow ^{263}_{105}\text{Db} + 3n$

   $^{22}_{10}\text{Ne} + ^{244}_{95}\text{Am} \longrightarrow ^{262}_{103}\text{Lr} + ^{4}_{2}\text{He}$

   $^{22}_{10}\text{Ne} + ^{244}_{95}\text{Am} \longrightarrow ^{266}_{106}\text{Sg} + e^-$

5. $^{244}_{95}\text{Am} \longrightarrow ^{4}_{2}\text{He} + ^{263}_{105}\text{Np}$

   $^{263}_{105}\text{Db} \longrightarrow e^- + ^{266}_{106}\text{Sg}$

   $^{262}_{103}\text{Lr} + e^- \longrightarrow ^{262}_{102}\text{No}$

   $^{266}_{106}\text{Sg} \longrightarrow ^{4}_{2}\text{He} + ^{262}_{104}\text{Rf}$

6. None of the isotopes are likely to be present at Earth's surface because they all have very short half-lives.

Math Skills Transparencies 41 – Balancing Nuclear Equations

1. 238 is the mass number of the isotope, and 92 is the atomic number of the isotope.

2. On the left side of the equation, the mass number of uranium is 238. On the right side of the equation, the sum of the mass number of thorium, 234, and the mass number of helium, 4, is also equal to 238. On the left side of the equation, the atomic number of uranium is 92. On the right side of the equation, the sum of the atomic number of thorium, 90, and the atomic number of helium, 2, is also equal to 92.

3. $^{69}_{31}\text{Ga}$

4. $^{204}_{82}\text{Pb}$

5. neutron

6. γ

7. 3 neutrons

8. $^{138}_{48}\text{Cd}$

9. $^{1}_{1}\text{H}$

Math Skills Transparencies 42 – Solving Half-Life Problems

1. $^{238}_{96}\text{Cm}$

2. 3.0 g̶/48.0 g̶ = 1/16 original amount; $1/16 = (1/2)^4$, or 4 half-lives = 4 × 3.5 min = 14 min

3. Amount remaining
   = 48.0 g × $(1/2)^{21.0 \text{ m̶i̶n̶}/3.5 \text{ m̶i̶n̶}}$
   = 48.0 g × $(1/2)^6$ = 0.750 g

4. $^{131}_{54}\text{Xe}$

5. When 60.0 g has decayed, 4.0 g remain; 4.0 g̶/64.0 g̶ = 1/16 original amount; 1/16 5 (1/2)4, or 4 half-lives = 4 × 8.0 d = 32 d

6. Amount remaining = 64.0 g × $(1/2)^{56 \text{ d̶}/8.0 \text{ d̶}}$ = 64.0 g $(1/2)^7$ = 0.50 g

7. $^{146}_{63}\text{Eu}$

8. Amount remaining = 72.0 g × $(1/2)^{290 \text{ d̶}/48.3 \text{ d̶}}$ = 72.0 g $(1/2)^6$ = 1.12 g

9. 9.00 g = 9.00 g/72.0 g = 1/8 = $(1/2)^3$; 3 half-lives = 3 × 48.3 d = 145 d

Study Guide - Chapter 24 – Nuclear Chemistry

Section 24.1 Nuclear Radiation

1. X ray

2. radiation

3. radioactivity

4. radioactive decay

5. radioisotope

6. gamma rays

7. alpha particles

8. beta particles

9. X rays

10. gamma ray

11. 0

12. Ernest Rutherford

13. 2+

14. 1−

15. 0

Section 24.2 Radioactive Decay

1. a

2. b

3. d

4. c

5. c

6. a

7. b

8. a

9. d

10. c

11. b

12. d

13. b

Section 24.3 Nuclear Reactions

1. true

2. false

3. true

4. false

5. true

6. true

7. false

8. false

9. true

10. false

11. false

12. true

13. false

14. false

15. true

16. true

17. true

18. fuel rods

19. B

20. control rods

21. C

22. A

23. the containment shell

24. a coolant

25. D

26. F

27. steam generator

28. E

29. G

30. H

31. false

32. false

33. true

34. true

35. true

36. true

37. false

38. false

39. true

40. false

41. true

Section 24.4 Applications and Effects of Nuclear Reactions

1. o

2. j

3. d

4. b

5. n

6. i

7. k

8. f

9. a

10. l

11. m

12. h

13. e

14. g

15. c

Chapter Assessment - Chapter 24 – Nuclear Chemistry

Reviewing Vocabulary

1. i

2. m

3. a

4. f

5. p

6. b

7. l

8. e

9. n

10. q

11. g

12. c

13. o

14. d

15. k

16. h

17. j

Understanding Main Ideas (Part A)

1. a

2. c

3. c

4. a

5. d

6. b

7. d

8. c

9. a

10. b

Understanding Main Ideas (Part B)

1. a. beta emission

b. positron emission or electron capture

c. alpha emission

d. beta emission

e. positron emission or electron capture

f. gamma emission

2. a. n fusion

b. $^{139}_{54}$Xe fission

c. $^{2}_{1}$H fusion

d. $^{149}_{57}$La fission

e. $^{233}_{92}$U fission

3. a. $^{58}_{27}$Co

b. $^{1}_{1}$P

c. $^{59}_{26}$Fe

d. γ

Thinking Critically

1. $^{2}_{1}$H

2. $^{56}_{26}$Fe

3. 8, on a scale of 1-10

4. at the beginning and the end of the table

5. The combination of two lighter nuclei produce a heavier nuclei with a larger mass number that will be more stable than the lighter nuclei.

6. During nuclear fission, a large nucleus breaks apart into two smaller nuclei, each of which is likely to be more stable than the heavier nucleus.

Applying Scientific Methods

Radioisotope	Decay Scheme	Half-life	Predicted Order of Abundance
Thorium-232	Alpha emission	1.4×10^{10} years	1
Radium-228	Beta emission	6.7 years	2
Actinium-228	Beta emission	6 hours	5
Thorium-228	Alpha emission	1.9 years	3
Radium-224	Alpha emission	3.6 days	4

1. $^{232}_{90}\text{Th} \longrightarrow {}^{4}_{2}\text{He} + {}^{228}_{88}\text{Ra}$

$^{228}_{88}\text{Ra} \longrightarrow \beta + {}^{228}_{89}\text{Ac}$

$^{228}_{89}\text{Ac} \longrightarrow \beta + {}^{228}_{90}\text{Th}$

$^{228}_{90}\text{Th} \longrightarrow {}^{4}_{2}\text{He} + {}^{224}_{88}\text{Ra}$

$^{224}_{88}\text{Ra} \longrightarrow {}^{4}_{2}\text{He} + {}^{220}_{86}\text{Ra}$

2. answer shown in table above

3. The isotope with the longest half-life would occur in the greatest abundance because it takes longest for it to decay.

4. Radiation A is beta radiation because it is attracted to the positive electrical plate.

5. Radiation B is gamma or X radiation because it is unaffected by either electrical plate.

6. Radiation C is alpha radiation because it is attracted to the negative electrical plate and has greater momentum (mass) than radiation D.

7. Radiation D is positron because it is attracted to the negative electrical plate and has less momentum (mass) than radiation C. Its track is also identical to that of radiation A, except bent in the opposite direction.

8. The deuterons would be attracted to the negative electrical plate and would form a track between those of the positron and alpha rays.

9. The track of the oxygen ions would bend toward the positively charged plate and travel farther out than the beta radiation track.